OTHER PEOPLE

OTHER PEOPLE

Portraits from the Nineties

D J TAYLOR & MARCUS BERKMANN
Illustrated by Charles Griffin

BLOOMSBURY

First published in Great Britain 1990

The moral right of the authors has been asserted.

Bloomsbury Publishing Ltd, 2 Soho Square, London W1V 5DE

A CIP catalogue record for this book
is available from the British Library.

ISBN 0 7475 0724 4

10 9 8 7 6 5 4 3 2 1

Typeset by Hewer Text Composition Services, Edinburgh
Printed in Great Britain
by Butler and Tanner Ltd, Frome and London

The figures who populate *Other People* have few shared characteristics. Some are wildly successful, others not; some are fixed firmly in the public eye, others conspicuously out of it. What unites them is their indisputable status as products of our age.

Lord Trimmer the superannuated peer; Denise the fading glamour model; Upminster Barry; Steve Brand, corporate gamester; Max and the Oxford Street irregulars; Mrs D'Souza and her hotline from God. These are the 'other people' – the characters we see around us, some of them swimming strongly through the current, others flotsam and jetsam on the tide of the 1990s.

In these sharply observed and provocative sketches, D. J. Taylor and Marcus Berkmann have assembled a gallery of recognisable modern characters: 'other people' maybe, but firmly attached to our own personal lives. Perhaps, in the last instance, they are not 'other people' at all . . .

Foreword

This book owes its inspiration to *Modern Types* by the late Geoffrey Gorer, with illustrations by Ronald Searle, first published by the Cresset Press Ltd in 1955.

These pieces are about types, not individuals. Any resemblance to a living person and any use of a real name is entirely inadvertent.

D.J.T.

M.B.

Contents

OTHER PEOPLE

Barry

One of the things Barry is certain of is his exact status in life. Casual observers, those people who sit next to him in restaurants or occupy the same railway carriage, might hastily mark him down as a yob – game Barry with his tousled rug of a haircut and his hod-carrier's forearms – but this would be a mistake. Barry is not a yob, yobs being characterised by their inability to 'do the business'. Neither is he a hooligan, whose activities he looks upon frowningly as 'well out of order'. Barry is a *lad*.

The distinction is an important one: in fact, the whole structure of modern youth culture might be said to hinge on such gradations. For compared to 'your average street-corner tosser' Barry is an altogether superior article, the possessor of a car ('two years old, two grand, no trouble'), a job as a despatch driver ('cash on the table, no trouble') and even, somewhere way back, an educational qualification. In the image-conscious circles in which he moves these advantages are perilously ignored. For whereas the yob is deserving only of general contempt, the lad has a definite status, a tangible allure, abetted by newspapers and the existence of innumerable popular icons. Several first-division footballers are lads, as are a number of pop stars, especially the hard-drinking, fan-impregnating ones. Comedians with Cockney accents are lads. Ian Botham is a lad.

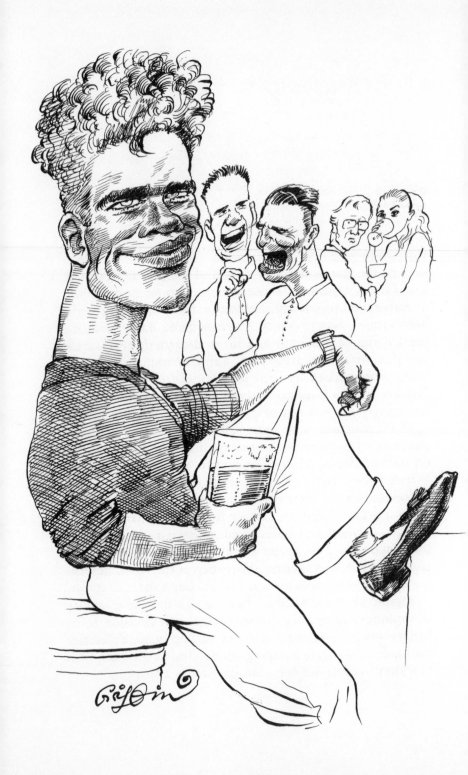

At several removes from these remote exemplars, Barry's laddery is of a fairly typical cast. It takes in attendances at the larger London soccer grounds: Spurs, Arsenal – Chelsea even, if the big clubs are away – and appearances at nightclubs. It embraces foreign holidays, community singing in pubs, noisy interventions in public places and tenpin bowling with milk bottles late at night in seaside towns. It is aggressive rather than violent (Barry is contemptuous of 'real nutters' who 'go looking for trouble'). By the same token it rarely extends to outright criminality. Like most of his associates Barry is permanently 'on the fiddle' and has never paid income tax in his life, but he would probably stop short of hitting a policeman.

There are several other Barrys in this particular part of Upminster – smart semi-detacheds with the occasional Jag idling on the verge – and as a result his social life is agreeably diverse. Barry and his mates are not quite up to organised activities – an 18-plus group or a Club 18–30 holiday would be a bit beyond them – but they do like collective amusement: drinking (Bacardi for preference, lager if the funds are low), pub games, the occasional excursion Up West for a boxing match (Terry Marsh, before his downfall, was the *ne plus ultra* of laddery and they used to follow him around), or the clubs. Women, curiously, play a relatively minor part in these activities. Like everyone else, of course, Barry has 'an eye for the birds' and would, as he puts it, 'shag a pig in knickers' if the opportunity presented itself, but these are boys-only affairs and the occasional presence of a strong-stomached girlfriend is tolerated rather than encouraged.

Taken together, Barry and his 'team' – Stan, Trevor, Fat Eric and the others – are a peaceable crowd, welcomed by landlords and restaurant owners alike for the large amounts of money they have at their disposal (Barry will spend £50 a night on his amusements if he feels like it, and quite often does). However, this air of collective absorption can be deceptive. These are tough boys, remember, tough boys from Essex. Ask them to turn the noise down or remember that there are ladies present, as the unwary occasionally do, and you are quite likely to get an elbow in the face or, at the very least, a pint of beer upended over your head. To give Barry and the rest of the lads their due, these outbursts stem less from any innate malice than from a deep, unreflective solidarity, liable to convert a momentary personal slight into an immediate collective grudge. Barry's own verdict is that he 'wouldn't hurt a fly' unless, as he puts it, 'the geezer really asked for it'. He is mocked with impunity.

Walk into a pub in Hornchurch, Dagenham or Romford, linger for a while in one of the turbulent roadhouses on the A13 down towards Shoeburyness and you can be pretty sure of seeing Barry poised over the snooker table or jamming fifty-pence pieces into the video jukebox. The chances are, however, that you will fail to recognise him. In his early twenties, youthful facial lines already filling out, dressed in the standard off-duty lad outfit (short-sleeved shirt, canvas trousers, fake Guccis) he is a curiously generalised figure. Five years of hectic, indiscriminate laddery have had a predictable effect on what was never a very distinctive personality: honing the studiously Cockneyfied diction, deadening the weight of second-hand anecdote and opinion. To do Barry justice, he is neither incurious nor unobservant. Neither does he harbour many of the prejudices habitually ascribed to him by left-wing newspapers. He reads the *Daily Mirror* rather than the *Sun* and if he were not disenfranchised (the family is making heroic efforts to avoid the Poll Tax) would certainly vote Labour. Similarly, though the team might make extravagant jokes about Jews and Negroes, these seldom harbour any deep-seated convictions, and Barry has several 'ethnic' acquaintances with whom he is on terms of considerable amity. Oddly only the whiff of inversion inspires him to genuine rancour. For some reason Barry and his mates reserve their deepest contempt for 'gay boys' or 'wrong 'uns' and their rare punch-ups tend to be provoked by the sight of an earring across the bar or the glimpse of an entwined pair of male fingers.

It is not quite certain what will become of Barry. He might go on being a lad for ten or twenty years – Barry's dad, it should be said, is still a lad at fifty – or he might not. Despite the strength of his allegiances – he will happily give up a day's work to accompany the team on some hastily arranged excursion – he is not unambitious and the despatch job will soon be jettisoned in favour of something more lucrative in the driving line, taking up more of his time but providing more money for clothes and entertainment. Alternatively, he may settle for domesticity. (Barry thinks marriage is 'a mug's game', but if the situation demanded it he would probably do the decent thing.) When not 'out on the piss' or merely 'hanging around' – in fact, when separated from his companions – he has much to recommend him. He is capable of considerable affection, notably to his parents, who indulge him horribly, but also to occasional girlfriends; is never tightfisted with money and is apt to turn mildly sentimental in the company of children. In fact the besuited tube traveller disposed to sneer at Barry's frothy haircut and his unfurled tabloid would do much better to envy him. For, strangely, Barry has two conspicuous advantages over his fellows. First – a consequence, perhaps, of his complete lack of introspection – he is highly attractive to women. Second, and even more inexplicably, he is entirely content.

D.J.T.

5

Ken Rubber

Far from the glamorous arenas of Fleet Street and its dockland outposts, several careers' length from even the obscurest literary weekly, lie uncharted wastelands of journalistic endeavour unimaginable to the sheltered reader. Trade magazines and technical journals, known to few and read by fewer, provide employment for thousands of eager newshounds yet to astonish a wider readership with their vital and incisive prose. This is the world of *Tunnels And Tunnelling*, of *Large Mixed Retailing* and *World Potato*, of *The British Goat Society Monthly Journal*.

Ken Rubber is editor of *Sheet Metal Weekly* and, at forty-eight, a well known authority on all things sheet metallic. On the infrequent occasions that sheet metal is a subject of topical interest, Rubber is telephoned by national newspapers and asked to supply expert wisdom and punditry. An intelligent and articulate man, he finds this little strain. He has even been on Radio 4.

Behind this superficial portrait of success and contentment, however, Ken is not the happiest of men. Though his status as Mr Sheet Metal is secure and, in a small way, prestigious, it is not what he set out to achieve. Nonetheless, Ken is a traditionalist, and like many a disappointed journalist, has chosen drink as his means of salvation. By 11:30 he can usually be found in his seat at The Fretful

6

Porpentine, a central London pub. At 3:30, in a mellower mood, he returns to his corner at *SMW* for a well-earned siesta.

It would not be unreasonable to assume from this behaviour that *Sheet Metal Weekly* is in terminal decline; in fact it flourishes. Ken's deputy, an able twenty-eight-year-old who is beginning to apply for posts elsewhere, manages to cover for her leader's idiosyncratic habits by the simple expedient of doing both of their jobs. A further seven journalists, with titles like 'Assistant Editor (Aluminium)', burrow efficiently in the arid terrain of sheet metal, all waiting for Ken to be fired so that they can each move up one notch in the *SMW* hierarchy.

But Ken is lucky. An old army friend is Editorial Director of the magazine group (which includes *Bathrooms Bulletin* and *Local Authority Architect*), and he feels that Ken's problems are temporary, can be solved, and anyway don't seriously affect the running of the magazine. Besides, *Sheet Metal Weekly* is profitable. Its news reporting is efficient, its features praise innumerable important men in suits and, crucially, it carries pages and pages of advertising. Why change a winning team?

The magazine's journalists, particularly Ken's able twenty-eight-year-old deputy, are less convinced. Yet there is no obvious replacement. The two or three staff members with any scintilla of talent will soon be off anyway, to more interesting jobs. The rest are not up to it. The company prefers to promote from within. For the moment, at least, Ken appears to be safe.

Life has not always been so perilous. He started late in journalism, after a successful military career that had been extended beyond the natural bounds of national service. His stories of honour and achievement, recounted in bars and rarely believed, are usually only slightly embellished versions of the truth. Ken was indeed the youngest major in NATO for a period, having risen swiftly through the ranks. It was a substantial achievement for someone of modest background, but Ken was exceptionally bright. His ordered personality, logical mind and ability to inspire loyalty suited the army, and the army suited him. Moving into administration (owing to an unfortunate shortage of wars), he developed an interest in computers, a distinction that seemed likely to earn him yet further promotion.

But at thirty-two, Ken suddenly realised that he had missed the sixties. Then, as his commission came up for renewal, his wife, bored of army life, left him. Ken resigned. Within weeks he had a job on *Mainframe News* and was growing his hair.

Ken began to catch up with what he had been missing. He found journalism a satisfying challenge, and distinguished himself with a series of warmish scoops that other dozier papers had missed. Within three years he was editor of his paper, a short step (to the pub, in fact, for an 'interview' with his old army chum) to the top job on the nascent *Sheet Metal Weekly*.

His decline was gradual – at first he didn't even notice it himself. By 1978, though, his second wife had ejected him from the marital home in favour of her chiropodist, and the famous Rubber nose was beginning to flower, growing ever redder and more bulbous as the years passed. Inexplicably a third wife was recruited.

Or perhaps not entirely inexplicably. When sober, Ken can be both cogent and charming, his brain apparently unaffected by years of abuse. Even now, traces of his youthful good looks remain visible in poor light. The rest of his body, though, has long since surrendered to the inevitable ravages. Most afternoons he dozes peacefully at his desk, resting his head on layers of unread press releases, cigarette ash, crushed coffee cups and editorial proposals for 1981. He has recently divorced yet again and is staying at a nearby YMCA. Occasionally children from his various marriages phone up for money, and PR girls ring to invite him to irrelevant press functions, which he attends. He is having an affair with the editorial assistant, 19.

Throughout his fall, Ken's friends have stayed remarkably loyal and sympathetic. He is still respected by some colleagues and minions, if not revered as in the past. His favourite staff member on *SMW*, though, is Doug Relish, a sullen ex-soldier (dishonourably discharged, although Ken doesn't know that) with whom he discusses military manoeuvres after work in The Fretful. Ken is grooming him for greater responsibility, a mistake because Relish is unpopular, untrustworthy and barely competent at his job. Even the Editorial Director cannot tolerate him, so it may be Ken's tireless lobbying that finally abbreviates his own career. Not that he would necessarily mind. For as he slumbers, Ken dreams of the army and wars and comradeship and discipline, of battles about more than just circulations. For Ken is a man out of time: in all his military career he never had to fight.

M.B.

Mrs Verdant Green

Mrs Verdant Green's public pronouncements on the countryside, of which there are a great number, are both oracular and exhortatory. 'We have to make our opinions *heard*' she is fond of saying, or 'it's up to us to shoulder our responsibilities'. Depending on the nature of her audience, she may go on to mention 'rural solidarity' or 'the value of *collective* action'. She has even, in very exalted flights, been known to talk about 'urban blight'. Mrs Verdant Green's listeners, a Townswomen's Guild coffee morning or a gathering of parish councillors, are occasionally alarmed by the violence of these remarks – Mrs Verdant Green is very strong on 'bureaucrats', government ministers and any institution thought to be 'despoiling our heritage' – but there is no denying the force of her oratory. Should a collection be called for – and Mrs Verdant Green is an advocate of what she calls 'paying for our principles' – some of them have been known to subscribe as much as five pounds.

Mrs Verdant Green's connection with the various bodies and interest groups which she addresses in this way is long-standing. She is chairwoman of the county branch of the Campaign for the Preservation of Rural England and secretary of the district National Heritage Trust, as well as administering a number of less widely known

local organisations concerned with the upkeep of wild-fowl sanctuaries and beauty spots. It is a laborious business, demanding the constant deployment of her time and energies – Mrs Verdant Green is rather contemptuous of 'so-called enthusiasts' who presume to 'manage a campaign from an armchair' – but her pursuit of what she refers to as her 'ideals' is indefatigable. Mrs Verdant Green would call herself an 'activist' if the word were not so disagreeably suggestive of striking mineworkers. At the very least she regards her role as that of a social catalyst, someone able to 'stir people's consciences' and encourage them to believe that 'what they do *can* make a difference'. With her brisk manner and her sensible countrywoman's clothes, moleskin jackets and tweed skirts – Mrs Verdant Green always looks as if she had recently alighted from a Land Rover – she cuts an impressive public figure.

These are busy times, of course, for those concerned with the preservation of rural glory: there are trunk roads being built, houses being thrown up, forests wilting beneath the woodman's axe, and the need for Mrs Verdant Green's energising powers has increased rather than diminished. Fortunately her leisure time has expanded to the point where it can accommodate these new demands. In the past, weighed down by domestic commitments, Mrs Verdant Green did not perhaps have as many hours as she wished to devote to 'the cause'. Now, with the children grown up and living elsewhere, her time is predominantly her own and she will frequently devote whole days to protest meetings concerning the route of Channel Tunnel rail links or public hearings convened to discuss motorway extensions (Mrs Verdant Green is somewhat imperious at these times and invariably succeeds in catching the chairman's eye).

The sympathy which Mrs Verdant Green extends on these occasions to 'the countryside' and those engaged in 'rural pursuits' is generous but not, it should be said, indiscriminate. It is all, Mrs Verdant Green thinks, a question of 'values', a matter of appreciating 'the true spirit of the countryside'. Her own appreciation of the true spirit of the countryside is finely judged. If there is a single quality whose existence Mrs Verdant Green deplores in her fellow activists it is 'sentimentality', whether applied to animals, agricultural methods or more marginal rural activities. As a result she staunchly approves of fox-hunting, battery farming, pheasant rearing and horsewhips and remains deeply suspicious of their opponents, none of whom quite understands 'the realities of country life', and many of whose activities are 'downright sinister'. Mrs Verdant Green is reduced to silent fury by the descriptions of the hunt saboteurs which she reads about in *Horse and Hound* and can frequently be heard to suggest that 'something should be done about them'.

By nature Mrs Verdant Green is a kindly woman; consequently these excoriations sit oddly with the more vivid expressions of a thoughtful and generous temperament. Their explanation lies, perhaps, in her upbringing. Mrs Verdant Green was born, as she unhesitatingly puts it, into the 'officer class', spending much of her early life in the vicinity of Catterick, where her father was a staff captain. Undoubtedly such a status implied (as did her subsequent nurture) a wide knowledge of country matters, but unhappily Mrs Verdant Green discovered that this knowledge was largely theoretical. Theoretically she knew how to load and fire a shotgun, but practically her father's rank denied her invitations to the local shoots. Theoretically she knew how to ride a horse and instruct a groom, but practically her parents could scarcely afford the lessons. Excluded, by dint of poverty, from gymkhanas and moorland slaughter Mrs Verdant Green cultivated a vicarious attachment to these activities that was perhaps more intensely felt than would have been the experience of actual participation. The knowledge which she picked up at this time, again notional rather than actual, endures. Though never more than an avid spectator, she knows more about point-to-points than most point-to-point riders and she remains an authority on 'the chase' (her name for fox-hunting). Frequently this immersion in 'country lore' verges on the pedantic: Mrs Verdant Green delights, for example, in informing the unknowing that huntsmen's coats are 'pink' rather than red and that the name comes not from their colour but from the Mr Pink who invented them.

Such knowledge was all very well, but by her early twenties Mrs Verdant Green had grown keenly conscious that it would not do. Neither would any of the callow subalterns of her father's regiment who had so far expressed an interest in her attractions (Mrs Verdant Green was at this time habitually referred to as 'a fine-looking girl', but then this is a description which can also be applied to racehorses). Despairing of Catterick, Mrs Verdant Green departed for London, took a secretarial job with the English Landowners' Association, met Mr Verdant Green at a party and, in keeping with the traditions of her class, ordered him to marry her. Fortunately Mr Verdant Green, a youngish property developer with 'prospects', obliged. There was nothing said during the course of their rather brief engagement about 'second homes' or 'rural retreats' – although she is fond of calling a spade a spade Mrs Verdant Green can be euphemistic when she chooses – but significantly her first decisive act as a married woman was to instruct Mr Verdant Green to subscribe to *Country Life*.

Marriage, Mrs Verdant Green has discovered, is not an unalloyed blessing. It has provided her, to be sure, with three healthy children whom she treats with an inherited combination of indulgence and severity, and afforded her a surprisingly comfortable standard of living (Mr Verdant

Green's speculations in the property line proving successful in a manner his wife had scarcely anticipated), and yet . . . Thirty years on from the Verdant Greens' arrival at their capacious dwelling place in Ewell village, Mrs Verdant Green can still not quite conceal her disappointment at being compelled to live in Surrey, within commuting distance of Mr Verdant Green's office in Waterloo, or forgive her husband for this compulsion. To be sure, there is a view over the Downs and the house is manorial in aspect, but Mrs Verdant Green is aware that these are entirely bogus considerations. County, after all, is county and Mrs Verdant Green views her London telephone number with something approaching despair. A similar attitude is extended to quasi-rural local amenities, notably the North-West Surrey Hunt, whose activities Mrs Verdant Green apostrophises contemptuously as 'hunting over dustbins'.

There are compensations, of course. There is 'her' parish church, whose flower arrangements and harvest festivals she is pleased to supervise, and 'her' parish council meetings, where her opinions on the encroachment of the London overspill find a deferential audience (in Mrs Verdant Green's vocabulary there is no more widely used pejorative than 'suburban'). Yet it is a fact that the happiest periods of her life are spent not at home, or running 'her' dogs – sensible retrievers and Airedales – over Epsom Downs, but on the rare occasions, perhaps two or three times a year, when her husband takes her to stay at the reconditioned manor house in North Yorkshire used by his firm to entertain its clients. At these times, supported by the staff (there is only a daily in Ewell) and with an audience unfamiliar with country ways, it may be said that Mrs Verdant Green experiences a sense of unparalleled inner satisfaction. Something of this air of serenity occasionally communicates itself to Mr Verdant Green, but he is an unimaginative man and merely attributes the transformation to a change of scene. It is not all plain sailing, however, and it must be admitted that there are certain activities associated with her stay which Mrs Verdant Green does not regard with complete enthusiasm. Still, somebody has to disembowel the pheasants and gut the hares and to decline, as Mrs Verdant Green argues fiercely to herself, would be a sad negation of a countrywoman's duty. It is wholly in keeping with Mrs Verdant Green's character that such squeamishness genuinely appalls her. At such times she perseveres gamely in her attempts to emulate a way of life of which she has such a fervent, if possibly rather limited, appreciation.

D.J.T.

Dominic Quintin

Londoners of socialistic bent have often aroused the envy of their provincial peers. While northern ideologues have no choice but to ascribe their every grievance to 'those southern bastards', the capital's assorted Trotskyists and anarcho-syndicalists have an agreeably wide variety of people on hand to hold in contempt. The advertising industry, the judiciary and the Metropolitan Police are all based in London, along with the civil service, the Freemasons and the *Daily Express*. But of all society's villains, one particular sector of capitalistic activity has in recent times been pre-eminent. For gross moral turpitude (and indeed vast wealth), no one can match those most visible beneficiaries of Thatcherite deregulation, the New Young Rich of the City.

Dominic Quintin is one such. At twenty-eight, armed with a public school face and an impeccable taste in ties, he has already fulfilled all of his – and his parents' – career expectations with spectacular success. He was always destined to be a banker, of course, and after Cambridge passed easily into a prestigious job at an august City establishment. He soon distinguished himself by being exactly like everyone else who worked there; more money, larger cars and ever quieter suits followed as a matter of course. As salaries rose around him, he moved from

17

bank to bank, each time negotiating an ever-improving
'package' for himself. For his current job at Credit Suitte
First Baltimore, he has upgraded to a natty black BMW
and an annual income that lies around halfway between
what he needs and what he really wants.

The money markets are a closed and arcane world,
obscurantist in their jargon and, to all but 250,000 *Financial
Times* readers, entirely mysterious in their activities. To
Dominic's few non-banker friends – and they grow fewer
– his job is hard to pin down. 'What do you actually *do*,
Dom?' they cry, only to be lectured about put options and
PE ratios. Dominic is very interested in banking, and talks
about it a great deal. He regularly meets fellow bankers in
City wine bars after work (when he can get away) to discuss
banking and, more pertinently, its remuneration. Nigel, it
seems, has moved to Aykroyd and Belushi for another
£8,000 plus performance-related bonuses every other day
and a slightly larger BMW, while poor Sebastian, who was
at Magdalene, is only on £42,000 plus cheap mortgage and
. . . so on and so forth.

Dominic is tall, nearly good-looking and perfectly
presented. Years of rugby and school cross-country runs
have left a healthy complexion and a physique that will soon
turn to flab. His political leanings are unreconstructed Tory.
Pompously right-wing in his sixth form, he veered leftwards
at university, standing for office in several trivial elections
and even winning some of them. Skills learnt in Cambridge
politicking – ruthlessness, condescension, manipulation –
recommended him for a career in the City, where his
left-wing ideals were swiftly jettisoned.

Although a homosexual past is rumoured, Dominic now
lives with Nicola in a converted flat in Kentish Town.
Members of second-division pop groups and a Booker Prize
runner-up live in the same road. Dominic bought the flat
five years ago: its breathtaking rise in value in subsequent

years was one of his few non-City subjects of conversation, at least until the property boom ceased. Nicola, a relatively inexpensive acquisition whose appreciation has been less spectacular, is taken more for granted. They met soon after university, where they had unknowingly been contemporaries, and moved in together three months later. Their relationship has survived, not through any inherent compatibility, but because they met at a time in their lives when such a relationship – now based more on dinner parties and cleaning ladies than on genuine affection – was more likely to last than not. Marriage has been discussed, in an adult, disinterested sort of way; but nothing more has been done.

Their flat, with two bedrooms and a well-tended garden (not, naturally, by Dominic), is rather more spacious, and so more valuable, than those of their friends. Nevertheless, Dominic likes to tell everyone, they remain 'catastrophically undermortgaged', and plan to buy 'a little place in the country for the weekends'. For the moment, they satisfy themselves with subtle displays of conspicuous consumption. Rarely used TV and video (for taping miniseries and *The City Programme*) sit beside the sleekest in expensive compact disc players (Phil Collins, Sade) opposite a luxuriant American sofa and glass coffee table. The bookshelf is home to several well-tended house plants. Dominic has little time to read anything these days other than interviews with himself in banking magazines.

Inevitably, Nicola's career has been overshadowed by her boyfriend's achievements. She too works in a bank, but at a lower level, her ambition having long been muted by Dominic's success. The couple's combined income, nevertheless, is substantial: problems arise only in finding the time in which to spend it. Long hours of hard concentration leave Dominic exhausted in the evening, especially after his coronary-inducing game of squash. But 'work hard, play hard' is his motto, and he'll often move on from the squash club bar to an extortionate Japanese restaurant, from where he will later ring the bank to find out what the Dow Jones closed at. Dinner parties also take up much of his and Nicola's time – especially Nicola's time, poor darling – although Dominic's fund of amusing banking anecdotes does tend to frighten off the unwary these days.

All seems rosy. It is just as well, then, that Nicola has yet to notice a slight froideur in Dominic's attitude to her. Perhaps they are never alone long enough for it to register. Dominic's work is proving increasingly stressful, and occasionally he finds himself unable to cope without the aid of artificial stimulants. As time has gone on, these stimulants have grown more powerful and less legal. Nicola doesn't know, and he would rather she didn't find out. She would not approve; he resents her for that. He is not spending too much on it, yet. But he will. And it would be such a pity if this external factor should disturb, let alone destroy, the easy convenience of their life together. Wouldn't it?

M.B.

Ian Callow

Sometime very soon Ian is going to do something 'really creative'. Although he has yet to decide what shape this creativity will take – it might be a book of poems, a novel or even an appearance on the stage of the local repertory theatre – neither he nor the friends with whom he discusses these projects are in any doubt that the result will have 'a really big impact' and make people 'really sit up'.

These discussions take place at the most incongruous hours and in the most unlikely circumstances: early in the morning in bedsitting rooms which echo to the thump of distant record players; late at night in licensed premises thick with cigarette smoke. As Ian is employed by the administrative department of a regional arts association, they could plausibly take place during office hours, but for some reason he is chary of discussing his 'work' with colleagues. In any case there are not many other fledgling poets or tyro playwrights on the staff of Loamshire Arts – though there are a number of efficient young women with degrees in arts management – and Ian doubts whether they would make what he calls 'a suitable audience'.

Finding a suitable audience is a duty by which Ian and his friends are considerably exercised. Most of their leisure hours, in fact, are consumed in a search for people who are 'on the same wavelength' or might be thought to share their somewhat specialised tastes in art and literature. Regrettably, in a provincial city with a single arts centre and a writers' group of irreproachable gentility the prospect of locating these kindred spirits is rather limited, but Ian and his friends persevere. Several of them are applying for jobs in London, but until such time as these applications prove successful they preserve a fine contempt for anything 'metropolitan', in particular its publishers and cultural pundits. Such contempt is perhaps their most obvious shared characteristic. Ian and his friends *know*, as surely as they know that the sun will rise tomorrow, that the editors of Bloomsbury are engaged in a 'conspiracy' to exclude provincial talent from its rightful eminence, and that this 'ganging up' is gleefully abetted by the reviewers who sift books for public consumption. They regard the rejection slips and the polite letters of refusal which their work inspires as proud scars, accumulated in a battle which they never had the slightest chance of winning.

It is not so many years since Ian was an undergraduate, but his relative youthfulness – he is not yet thirty – tends to come as a surprise to those who do not know him well. His hair began to march backwards some years ago – a process he rather welcomed at the time – and baldness, together with a badly trimmed beard, gives him the appearance of a considerably older man. Despite the semblance of age his dress still follows the pattern of his campus days, taking in voluminous greatcoats, collarless white shirts and elderly pairs of leather boots. His appearance is not so much untidy as purposefully unkempt. He smokes a great many hand-rolled cigarettes, the pipe which characterised his student days having been discarded as a deplorable affectation. He is unmarried.

This apparent maturity – like Mr Smallweed in *Bleak House* Ian seems never to have had a childhood – is enhanced by the position of authority he holds among his friends, most of whom are prepared to regard him as the possessor of considerable, if unacknowledged, talents, and all of whom are prepared to defer to his opinions. These are very definite. Ian is fond of talking, for instance, of the 'radical ideas' which are needed to enliven a world of contemporary arts enfeebled by the 'London coteries' and the backscratchers of Bedford Square. At the same time he has a low opinion of contemporary novelists, especially those who make any money from their works, on the grounds that they have irretrievably compromised themselves at the hands of a base commercialism. In their place he advertises the merits of a limited canon of 'genuine' writers, mostly foreign, predominantly obscure and, without exception, dead.

Ian came early to the world of literary aspiration. As an adolescent he had read widely – perhaps too widely – around his subject: certainly his juvenile poetry, the faultless parodies of Eliot and Pound, sat oddly amongst the sentimental verses of the school magazine. A very distinguished poet indeed examined his entry to a national poetry competition and commended its promise. He was eighteen at the time. Such recognition, coinciding as it did with questions of university entrance, was a powerful inducement. He abandoned the place at Cambridge and the Law degree – it was rather late in the day for grandiose gestures of this sort – and instead enrolled himself on an English Literature course at a Welsh university.

Even at this early stage Ian was blessed with talents other than precosity. Unusually for a student of literature, uniquely perhaps for a practitioner, he entered university (where he might be supposed to have learned something to his advantage) with his views of 'English' already fully formed. As opinions these were, if not absolutely untenable, then highly unfashionable. Broadly speaking they concerned the artist and the expression of his temperament through his art. Pedagogues might advertise the advantages of 'delicacy', 'reserve', 'concealment'; Ian wanted revelation, assertion, *voluptuousness*. For him a poem existed not as a palisade of allusion and deflection erected around an ambiguous core of meaning, but as the confession of a highly stylised personality. Such an attitude led occasionally to bizarre departures from the prevailing orthodoxies. Set down to study the writers of the later Victorian age, he preferred Dowson and Le Gallienne to Tennyson and Browning, Wilde and Beardsley to Kipling and Wells: he found them more 'authentic'. The same criteria applied to the literature of the postwar era. The world had had enough, he argued – and he argued it convincingly – of 'bourgeois' and typically 'English' reticence. It wanted newer and yet more 'authentic' voices which were capable of expressing their rage, their anger and the 'essential anarchism' of every genuine human temperament. It wanted Kerouac, Ginsberg, Creeley and Henry Miller, and it would put up – at a pinch – with William Burroughs.

What it did not want, regrettably, was the work of Ian Callow. It did not want his undergraduate poetry, machine-gun monologues in the style of Ginsberg's *Howl*, and it did not want the short stories in which he described his experiments with drugs. It did not want *Carcasses*, his long, passionate novel about a butcher who murders his deaf-mute son, and it did not want his verse play about genocide. Ian bore these rebuffs at first with nonchalance and then with fortitude. He knew that such productions were the honest expressions of his temperament. He knew too that he had put into them as much application and perseverance as he believed himself to be capable, spending long hours over his notebooks and wholly neglecting his class work. Having failed his degree he spent two years in a bedsitter grinding out a second unpublished novel before poverty and no longer indulgent parents compelled him to take the job with Loamshire Arts.

The succeeding years have done little to soften an abiding sense of personal frustration. These are not, Ian is fond of pointing out, good times for the writer. After all, in a dead society, which only the foolish would deny that we inhabit, what is there for the artist except resignation? Ian has never read Cyril Connolly and would probably not much like him if he did, but the line in *Enemies of Promise* about 'closing time in the gardens of the West' would undoubtedly force a wry smile of recognition. Ian knows that he has 'something to say', something which in a bygone age would have enabled him to 'make a name for himself', but he doubts 'in this day and age' the possibility of a friendly reception. For the last two years he has been working on a long verse drama concerned with the ethical consequences of the atom bomb. Perhaps a thousand lines are complete. In his gloomier moments he wonders if he will ever finish it.

It is a circumscribed and – despite the confraternity of the bedsitting room – rather lonely existence, this, but Ian is not unduly discontented. He has read enough English fiction of the late 1950s to know that there is, or was, such a thing as a 'provincial Bohemia' and fondly imagines himself to be a part of it. Fortunately he is not such a fool as to believe that his position is indefinitely sustainable. There has been in recent months a regrettable falling off among the other Loamshire Bohemians, who now have a tendency to get married or take more remunerative forms of employment elsewhere. While Ian deplores these defections they do not surprise him. It is, after all, a characteristic of art not to pay the rent. He occasionally comforts himself with the thought that, alone among his companions, he has remained 'true to his principles', what an only recently vanished age would call 'keeping the faith'. On the other hand there is the alarming thought that these principles may not have been worth very much to begin with. Meanwhile, there are still enough Bohemians available for the occasional rousing drunk-cum-poetry reading. At these times, cheered momentarily by alcohol and the recitation of a great deal of sub-Ginsberg verse, the knowledge that he will shortly do something 'really creative' is still enough to compensate for a great deal of wasted time and a large amount of honest resentment.

D.J.T.

Steve Brand

'Brand's the name, branding's the game,' shouts Steve Brand into his glass of house white, his exhilaration growing with every swig. In his double-breasted suit, Tie Rack tie and loafers (unsuccessfully concealing a pair of luminescent white socks), Brand is a satisfied man. Today he has been promoted, from a mere Product Manager, handling the more arcane promotional activities of a fading range of aircraft model kits, to Marketing Manager, in charge of the brand he has long desired – the top-selling Snugglebunch soft toys, including Uncle Snuggly himself. A celebration is in order.

Having therefore booked the largest possible table at the local wine bar, Corkers, Steve has invited the rest of the marketing department of Tols-Toys plc to share his triumph. All are there (except for the Managing Director, who 'looked in' earlier on his way to an urgent rendezvous with his mistress), and many are making a substantial effort to be seen enjoying Steve's success. One man's success is of course another man's thwarted ambition, but this is not the time to show it. There are few friendships at Tols-Toys – the overly trusting do not survive long – but even the most single-minded of the marketing staff recognise that there are occasions at which it is incumbent on them to be sociable, and so it is with Steve's night in Corker's. Nigel

Glant, who looks after the Thunderblast range of war toys, is telling a rather louche joke about a Page Three girl, and although most present know it by heart, all are enjoying it with exaggerated enthusiasm.

So, pausing only to shout 'Ciao' to his secretary (who has to meet her boyfriend at eight), Steve calls for two more bottles of house white (viciously chilled to conceal its unappetising flavour) and prepares to wield his company Amex card. He has plans for Uncle Snuggly. In fact, he intends to 'reactivate' the entire range, especially Gramplebumms, who has a 'low profile in the marketplace'. The aim, naturally, is to make Tols-Toys plc the largest and most successful toy company in the country, with Steve Brand as its marketing director. The current incumbent, a tired forty-five-year-old who increasingly lives only for his weekend lawnmowing, is unaware of these plans.

But at twenty-six, Brand is hungry for glory. Although his new job comes with a suitably phallic motor car (a Cavalier two-litre GTI with spoiler, no stripes) and an equally throbbing salary rise, he wants more and he wants it the day before yesterday. His smile, firm handshake and snooker player's complexion are testament to his single outstanding characteristic – determination. He may not be – as he frequently tells his girlfriend – too bright, too good-looking or too well-educated (his contempt for learning, despite a polytechnic degree in engineering, is absolute), but he is relentlessly determined. Indeed, in his pursuit of greatness, he is gradually stripping himself of all those character traits – unpredictability, irony, imagination – that might count against him in the long run. He plays the corporate game in the only way that seems sensible – by following the rules to the letter and waiting for everybody else to make the mistakes.

In essence, though, Brand is a Bloke by both temperament and background. His accent – a nasal agglomeration of vowel sounds from every part of the British Isles – is unidentifiable as anything other than generalised lower-middle or upper-working class. His hair, until recently short with a few curly wispy bits at the back, is now merely short. He owns a compact disc player, whose numerous flashing lights conceal a surprisingly low stand-ard of oriental workmanship. His current girlfriend, one of a rotating series of local girls named Kelly or Michelle, apprentice hairdressers and secretary/PAs with danger-ously overpermed hair and small eyes, will soon be encour-aged to give up her job, marry Steve Brand and have babies.

His colleagues, now gleefully digging into a 'Champagne-style' sparkling wine, view the rise of Brand with irritation, concern or indifference, depending on their seniority and powers of observation. One or two have seen people like him before. One Tols-Toys graduate, now the International Marketing Director of a multinational car hire firm, was well known for employing a headhunter on retainer, an extravagance that, in light of the stratospheric pay rises he has received since, has paid for itself many times over. Brand has the address of the headhunter in his diary.

Now he also has a good idea of when he will be needing it. As Marketing Manager he will be in a strong position to negotiate for the control of future brands (all the toys are designed and manufactured by the company's US parent corporation), and in an even stronger position to sort out Nigel Glant, his only serious rival for future preferment. Marketing is not an art, as some of his more high-minded colleagues would have it (Brand is a dedicated fan of the phrase 'ivory tower'), but a skill, to be acquired and then used. There are only certain ways of doing things – to try anything else is to waste time and resources.

Not surprisingly, Brand is considered a dull number cruncher by his less astute rivals, most of whom are less willing than he to spend their lives moving regularly from job to job and location to location, forging contacts rather than making friends. As he moves around the country, though, Brand steps further away from his origins, from his unemployed, Labour-voting father and his embittered, neighbour-fixated mother. Through job mobility, he has discovered the ability to reinvent himself as he wishes: his letters home, consequently, have become less frequent and almost entirely free of hard information. Kelly-Michelle, if he chooses the right one, will presumably have to meet his parents at some time, and will, he hopes, understand why no one else is likely to be given the opportunity.

Steve Brand, then, is on his way – quite where, he does not yet know, but he will get there, and long before most people realise. Perhaps later, when he reaches global or at least European levels of responsibility, he may get the chance to reinvent himself totally – to move to the USA and perhaps to Tols-Toys' American base in Slugsville, MA. Already, strange transatlantic slang is beginning to creep into his meagre vocabulary ('let's go gangbusters on this one, lads'), and a gleam unexpectedly appears in his eye whenever he uses words like 'stateside'. Whether anyone misses him, when he finally abandons his loafers for sneakers, is of course another matter entirely.

M.B.

Lord Trimmer

Well, if ambiguously, into his seventies (the *Who's Who* entry is guarded), Lord Trimmer, formerly Sir James Trimmer, Labour Member of Parliament for Barsetshire North, is still very much a public figure. Bluff, hale and mildly evasive he appears on radio programmes of the *Question Time* variety where even the most grudging of interlocutors treats him with respect (Lord Trimmer has been known to turn nasty). Televised discussions of by-election results or the latest ministerial resignation seldom fail to canvass a set of opinions which, over the years, have grown increasingly judicious. To these leisured expositions are added activities which enable Lord Trimmer to rise beyond simple punditry. He produces occasional volumes of memoirs which if they do not sell are at least charitably reviewed, while allowing their author to cast and recast the famous anecdote of how once, at a windy *al fresco* rally, Clement Attlee borrowed his hat. In the series of parliamentary awards hosted annually by *The Spectator* he is quite likely to win some sort of prize.

Strangely, despite this public avowal of his talents, despite excellent health and a sound digestion, despite the prospect of a serene old age in which he can continue to potter about the House of Lords or gently oversee the administration of an Oxford college, Lord Trimmer is an unhappy and comfortless man, the butt of much secret ignominy. It is all very well for Conservative peers to cheer his homely contributions to parliamentary debates, it is all very well for Sir Robin to say this and Sir Alistair to aver that, but as far as his own party is concerned Lord Trimmer's name is mud, and he knows it: an unpopularity that finds expression in a dozen subtle and ingenious insults. His occasional addresses to the party conference are met with stony silence from that part of the hall where sit the massed ranks of the constituency delegates. His oracular endorsements of party policy are met with no very great enthusiasm by its leaders. On his infrequent visits to university Labour clubs burly young men tell him that he is a traitor to his class and policemen are obliged to escort him from the campus.

The explanation of this unpopularity lies not in any disloyalty (Lord Trimmer has followed the Whip for forty years) or impropriety, but in the strange and paradoxical nature of a party which traditionally converts the alleged treachery of its leaders into an article of faith. Lord Trimmer, who was an effective secretary of state for Defence in the first Wilson administration and a slightly less effective Home Secretary in the second, is by no means the principal villain. His disadvantage is simply that he has survived. His contemporaries, those hard-faced men of the party demonology who forged pacts with the Liberals, who rewrote manifestoes and dined with Mr Jenkins, have shuffled away from the political arena, have died, defected or disappeared. Lord Trimmer, as the result of some capricious streak in his nature, remains – a conspicuous relict of a past which his younger colleagues would prefer to forget.

All this is very hard on a man of whom it is said, without irony, that he gave his life for his party. Born a year or so before the Great War into a Derbyshire mining family – a felicitous heritage as he was later to discover – Trimmer's early years were lived out in grinding poverty. His father died on the Somme. His mother went back into service, consigning her son first to the care of negligent relatives and, later, to a scarcely less congenial children's home. It was a pitiable childhood, suffused with poignant sensation: Lord Trimmer used to recall, in print and conversation, the effect that this maternal desertion had upon his temperament and the delinquency that was its result. He was redeemed by a precocious intellect which conveyed him from the state primary school where, as he recalled, lousy children had their heads regularly painted with iodine, to a local grammar and hence to a technical college where he studied engineering. Equally precocious was the youthful Trimmer's political development. He joined the Labour party in his teens – a decision taken on humanitarian rather than ideological grounds – and, having forsaken the technical college for the engineering shop, swiftly immersed himself in the organisation of a largely passive labour force. At twenty-three he was a branch official of the Engineering Workers' Union – a connection that was to sustain him for the greater part of his political career.

At this stage in his life his conception of socialism admitted no very precise analysis. He had read a few pages of Marx, and found him dull. The English Fabians – Cole, Webb and Shaw – he found remote and patronising. Political behaviour, he reasoned, was largely a matter of expediency, of overturning recognised injustices and righting palpable wrongs. If a child was starving then you gave it food; if that gift involved requisitioning food from someone more amply provided, then so much the better. It was a simple creed, easily extended to his own province of labour relations. Men worked too many hours, he argued, for insufficient reward, spent their leisure time in houses that were cramped and overcrowded, ate food that left them undernourished and enervated. Subsequent skimmings through Marxist theoreticians and economists tended, obscurely, to confirm him in this diagnosis.

In the era of *Love on the Dole* and Jarrow these were radical sentiments. Their result was a series of blacklistings from frightened employers and – once – an appearance in a police court. Yet along with this youthful fervour came the first signs of a pragmatism that was to distinguish Trimmer's subsequent career. In the great debates that animated the pre-war Labour party he erred heavily on the side of common sense. He supported Bevin against Lansbury, the rearmers against the pacifists, Churchill against Chamberlain, because only a simpleton, he thought, would not have done so. His political heroes at this time were Bevan and Sir Stafford Cripps. Those who preached revolution in the streets were fools. What the working man wanted, surely, was shorter hours and higher wages. A socialist nirvana beckoned, full of good cheer, companionship and the harnessing of capital to a benevolent state.

The war enhanced his prospects. Though he spent the greater part of it afloat, on a Royal Navy patrol launch, he was careful to maintain his trade union contacts: these secured him the nomination for the union-sponsored seat of Barsetshire North, a few miles from the place of his birth. In the 1945 General Election he won a decisive victory over a Conservative group captain and a Liberal nonconformist preacher. As a backbench MP his pragmatism continued. He supported Bevan, because of the National Health Service, but distrusted the voluble and self-confident Harold Wilson. As the 1950s came and Attlee grew old he was an early supporter of Gaitskell. Taxed with lack of principle, with a self-serving concern with career, he was indignant. Was it not a man's right to do what he could for himself? Aided by the friends of his youth, now risen to senior positions in the trades union movement, his power base was sufficient to brave the demise of Gaitskell (whom he mourned sincerely) and ingratiate himself with Gaitskell's successor. Wilson, more or less enthusiastically, gave him Defence.

Disagreeably, office dented for the first time Lord Trimmer's confidence in his own abilities. Though he knew already that Defence ministers are seldom popular within the Labour party, the criticism which his uncontroversial actions attracted was a source of bewilderment. When younger, left-wing colleagues denounced his purchase of gunboats or the propping up of beleaguered post-colonial regimes he lost his temper. Common sense told him that Russia was an enemy and America an ally. Prudence dictated that the country's defences should be securely maintained. Had not Nye himself feared going naked into the conference chamber? It was the same several years later when as a lethargic and disillusioned Home Secretary he was forced to consider the appeal of two pickets convicted of wounding a fellow worker on a building site. Lord Trimmer, with forty years of trades unionism behind him, upheld their sentences. The working man had to be protected, he argued, while certain sections of that year's party conference attempted to howl him down. But it was the winter of discontent, the last great crisis of the Callaghan government, that finished him off. For one who had so long preached the brotherhood of the working man, the helping hand, the pulling together, and the other optimistic catch phrases of his youth, the spectacle of closed hospitals and undug graves could not be tolerated. He resigned, assisted by a mild and fortuitous heart attack, took a knighthood and went to the back benches. A General Election later he retired to the Upper House. The Barsetshire North seat, fought by a bearded young trades union research official of whom he heartily disapproved, was lost to the Conservatives.

Succeeding years have not lessened Lord Trimmer's bewilderment. A generation of younger Labour MPs, plucked from colleges of further education and obscure quangos, treats him with amused tolerance. He has never been able to treat their leader with any seriousness. His constituency party, though purged of the Trotskyists who brought such misery to his later years as an MP, remains unforgiving: its annual dinner is a dismal affair, despite the anecdotes about Mr Attlee and his hat. Yet the malaise is more fundamental than this. It could be said in fact that Lord Trimmer is scarcely certain of the foundations of his own opinions. Lady Trimmer, a relic of the old Derbyshire days, voted Conservative at the last election (a fact given regrettable prominence in several newspapers). Even Mrs Thatcher is not entirely sure of his stricture. Common sense urges that the country ought to be defended, that President Bush ought to be supported. Why should the working man not be allowed to purchase his own council house? Or send his son to a grammar school? To these and other questions Lord Trimmer can supply only half-hearted responses. Seated in his customary nook in the Lords, high above the Opposition front bench, neatly placed to meet the speaker's eye, pictured at the party to launch *Fifty Years with Labour*, a soon to be remaindered volume, he is a profoundly disillusioned man. There are occasional rumours in the Sunday newspapers that he will defect or throw over the Whip: none but the foolish should believe them. Loyalty, to his workmates, his colleagues and ultimately to his party, was forever Lord Trimmer's chief characteristic. Even at this late stage he cannot quite bring himself to throw over an institution to which he has given, quite literally, the greater part of his existence.

D.J.T.

Pamela Pride

Pamela has never minded being a tall woman. Angular, hyperactive, she leans over her prey, and awaits his response. Will she bite his head off? Or, as her limbs thrash and slice through the air, will she absent-mindedly envelop his slender frame and crush him to death?

The only real snag with this diverting scenario is that the male thus threatened is Pamela's business client. If the meeting continues in this vein, it seems unlikely that he will be her client for much longer. Pamela's colleagues, one sweating with fear and the other inflamed with fury, are powerless to intercede: both are her juniors.

In the long term, of course, Action Strategy PR will survive Pamela Pride – but the next fifteen minutes look undeniably sticky. Pamela means well (throughout her life this phrase has inevitably preceded a thorough demolition of her personality and habits) but she is entirely convinced that she could run Grollock Storm Blinds Ltd rather more adroitly than P. B. Grollock, Esq. Unfortunately this is what she is telling him at the moment.

As we move into the final hour of her career in Action Strategy PR, it seems only timely to reflect on the path that has brought her to this curious impasse in the first place. Pamela Pride is thirty-five, but looks not a day over forty. Born into an expatriate family for whom moving

house was less an inconvenience than a hobby, she was schooled in Britain, her fees paid for by her father's bank. For all her enthusiasm and commitment, she did not excel academically, but this did not prevent her rising to the position of head of house and, for one brief term after her predecessor had had to leave under unfortunate circumstances, head of school. Her skills on the sports field – in her hands a hockey stick was an offensive weapon – proved an adequate consolation for her poor performances in the classroom.

It did not, however, help her get into university, and after she had failed to be accepted by Oxford, Cambridge, Exeter and Durham, she moved into her parents' London pied-à-terre and sought employment. Her father, whom she adored, had successfully instilled into her his slightly aimless passion for hard work, and her first employers – she worked, perhaps inevitably, as a secretary – found her remarkably mature, confident and worldly for her years.

Yet, perhaps just as inevitably, she soon became bored. She enjoyed the social milieu (based around SW1 and a series of satisfyingly overpaid boyfriends), but the job did not stretch her. She also found subservience unusually tiresome. All those years in Penang calling for large gins and new tennis balls had not prepared her for obeisance of any kind, and it was with all the self-control she could muster that she did not tell her various masters where they could insert their job and what they could do with it thereafter (though ladylike in the extreme, she had also inherited her father's rather salty turn of phrase).

But then she met Peter Pride. A cousin of someone's, or possibly an old schoolfriend of someone else's, Peter was, at thirty-five, slightly older than the rest of her set and, like her, much travelled. He had lived for years in KL, he knew the ropes in Jedda, he had even met her father once at an embassy function in Ceylon. True, he was a little dull, or even very dull, but he represented an opportunity, however unpromising, to escape the photocopier and the coffee machine. He was in the country for a six-month extended holiday; within five they had married.

For the next five years they moved around the globe from job to job. Peter Pride was an engineer, much respected and with excellent connections in the Middle and Far East. There was a lot of work around – bridges and dams galore, gleaming banks and new government buildings – and Peter's reputation (and wide knowledge of local customs) kept him fully and lucratively employed. Until, alas, he tripped over a lunch box one afternoon and fell off the top of an unfinished seventeen-storey skyscraper.

Pamela was extremely put out. Peter had hardly been the most enthralling husband in the world, or even in Chittagong, but she had much enjoyed being his wife. The expatriate community was one in which she felt very comfortable, but while wives had a valuable role within it, widows did not. At just twenty-seven, she had little choice but to return to England.

She was not without plans, though. Her best friend in Hong Kong, who had noticed how enthusiastically she exhorted her peers to contribute to the numerous charitable functions she had organised, suggested public relations as a career. Here, she explained, was a genuine opportunity for advancement. It was a young industry, and one that routinely employed women in other than lowly tasks, where 'secretary' could be a starting point rather than a career in itself. The only real prerequisite was self-confidence, a commodity Pamela had in abundance. She moved back to London, bought a flat with Peter's savings, and, having suitably embellished her CV, secured a job with a small but flourishing agency.

The company was owned by two women, Jilly Action and Ros Strategy, who had moved into PR in the fashion boom of the late sixties. They believed in hard work, and they believed that women worked harder than men, a prejudice confirmed by the regular exodus of their few male employees to the local pub at 5:30 pm. Women, they found, were enthusiastic, loyal and above all cheap. The company thrived.

Pamela's single-mindedness rapidly endeared her to her employers. She was also assisted in her rapid progress through the ranks by the high casualty rate amongst her contemporaries, most of whom left to marry and procreate. It was a source of astonishment to her that so many intelligent, able-bodied young women seemed to think of nothing but babies. Jilly and Ros thought similarly, and after two years appointed Pamela a director of the firm, with responsibility for clients including Sunfun Lounge Seats, Technobore Computers (UK) and Frotho washing-up liquid.

Unfortunately, the appointment appears to have freed Pamela from the self-restraint that characterised her early days with the company. While at all times deferring to Jilly and Ros, whose expertise she recognises and respects, she has begun to make life rather demanding for her underlings and, increasingly, her clients. This change of behaviour has overflowed into her personal life as well. Her boyfriend of two years' standing, a quantity surveyor no less uncharismatic than her first husband, cannot understand 'what has got into her'. But her schoolmates would not notice anything awry, and nor would her father's old servants, or the wives of her father's junior employees. Perhaps she will embark on a freelance career at some point in the future, but at the moment, as steam starts to issue forth from Mr Grollock's ears, Pamela Pride fearlessly approaches her fall.

M.B.

Denise Jones

'So you take *photographs*?' Miss Jones will ask, if met at a party. 'That's really interesting, isn't it?' Her voice, Essex accent not wholly vanquished, is confidential, loud but not obtrusive. 'So you write for a *newspaper*?' she will say later. 'I must come and talk to you.' The young man, who rests one hand on the collar of her fun fur, will smile at this disingenuousness, recognising that Miss Jones's public and private lives no longer have definable boundaries. As the evening progresses she will drink sparingly, combining this abstinence with unstinting conversation, and leave early amid a shower of excuses. 'A girl's got to get her beauty sleep.' 'Early start tomorrow morning.' Such evasions, which would be tedious coming from any other young woman, are likely in Miss Jones's case to be the literal truth.

Although you are unlikely to have met Denise Jones, her face will be vaguely familiar. It stares out at passers-by, singly or as one among a group of other faces, on advertisement hoardings. Juxtaposed with some item of manufacture – it might be a car, or a lawnmower, or a double bed – it appears on the type of calendar hung on garage walls, or sold from behind the counters of small newsagents. Its features – wide, symmetrical eyes, a slightly vapid smile corresponding to the English conception of 'beauty' – are

not immediately distinguishable, but there is a definition about them – something to do with the skilful use of cosmetics – that sets them apart from more wholesome but less marketable complexions. Miss Jones is a model.

Surprisingly, this career, sought after and potentially lucrative, came about almost by accident. Miss Jones was not, when adolescent, one of those girls whose photographs are sent by admiring mothers to national newspapers. She had no aspirations to beauty contests or to the 'Miss Lovely Legs' competitions which were occasionally advertised by women's magazines or the manufacturers of skin-care products. In fact it could be said that in her early life Miss Jones had no aspirations at all. Largely ignored by her parents, without the brothers and sisters who might have furnished sympathy or companionship, she spent a lonely childhood in which schoolgirl magazines about horseriding played a greater part than the cultivation of whatever physical attributes she might be supposed to have possessed. Yet these were undeniable. By the beginning of her nineteenth year Miss Jones's five-feet-ten-inch frame – a height which had previously been the source of some distress – had been complemented by generous breasts and a complexion shorn of the last ravages of acne. On the strength of this she acquired a boyfriend, employed by a camera shop, whose hobby was 'glamour photography'. Though at first reluctant to approve a suggestion which seemed vaguely indecent, Miss Jones was soon persuaded to become one of his subjects.

It would be an exaggeration to say that Miss Jones woke up to find herself famous. She did, however, wake up to find herself in the pages of a tabloid newspaper. Obviously such celebrity could not be ignored. Its immediate effect was a series of separations: from her parents' house in Harlow, from the freight-forwarding company for whom she had been compelled to work as a typist, and from the boyfriend (the last step was the only one which Miss Jones in any way regretted: she had been genuinely fond of him). Miss Jones removed herself to London, specifically St John's Wood, and has remained there ever since. Agreeably, she found that modelling harboured few of the drawbacks that she had associated with this most precarious of professions. She fell into the hands of an agent who neither exploited her nor ignored her, but arranged for her work which was not, she discovered, dependent on the distribution of sexual favours. She made several friends among similarly situated girls met at promotional functions and photographic studios. There was also the satisfaction (occasionally) of being recognised in the street.

But her new career, Miss Jones has discovered, is not an unmixed blessing. There is the flat, of course, and there are occasional working holidays in the exotic locations demanded by the sponsors of calendars, but there is also a great deal of exhausting labour, much of it poorly rewarded. Miss Jones works a sixty-hour week, up at six some days to shoot underwear catalogues in draughty studios in the East End, on her feet some evenings until midnight when required to sit, partially clothed, on the bonnet of the latest adornments to the Motor Show, or to attend the opening of a new restaurant or nightclub. The hours, as Miss Jones cheerfully explains, play hell with your complexion and would not be sustainable without occasional recourse to more or less legal stimulants. Such irregularity is also a bar to all but the most perfunctory social or private life. The young men Miss Jones meets during the course of her daily work are seldom content to pursue a relationship that consists of snatched half-hours between shoots or appointments at studios fifteen miles apart, and there is among them a distressing readiness to assume a moral laxity to which Miss Jones does not herself subscribe; one of the few characteristics, curiously, to survive her

transformation from the old Harlow days. Miss Jones
does not choose to avail herself of more readily available
consolations: she has grown rather too used to overfriendly
photographers. These deprivations are accepted as a necessary adjunct to an outwardly glamorous lifestyle.

There is also the problem of professional standards.
Almost uniquely among her contemporaries, Miss Jones
maintains a strict attitude to what she will and will not do.
'I don't mind taking my knickers off, but that's as far as it
goes. I won't do any of those shots where the girl has one
leg on either side of the room, and I won't do any pictures
with men – however much they're wearing.' Such rigour is,
professionally speaking, disadvantageous: several of Miss
Jones's contemporaries find this type of exposure, in cheap,
badly produced magazines where no one remembers a face,
an invaluable source of additional income, but at present
Miss Jones is not prepared to compromise her principles.
The same argument, by extension, applies to the few film
offers she has received: supporting roles in low-budget
features requiring her to cavort – albeit fictitiously – with a
succession of anonymous actors. The refusal of such work
has won her a disagreeable reputation for perversity.

But the greatest drawback is to do not with leering art
directors, or being asked to don rubber mackintoshes (a
staple of the 'amusing' photographs into which Miss Jones
is occasionally inveigled) but with the passing of time. At
twenty-five she might reasonably be supposed to have
reached her prime, but modelling girls are getting younger,
and the pages of the tabloids are crowded out with sixteen-
and seventeen-year-olds; 'meathook girls' Miss Jones calls
them. The resentment which Miss Jones and her colleagues
feel for these younger competitors springs from a distrust
not so much of age as of professional technique, a lack of the
subtlety which only experience can confer. 'I mean,' Miss
Jones will tell you, 'who wants to look at a picture of some

sixteen-year-old just staring at these bloody great things on her chest?' In the intervals of carping she is conscious that she has only a short time in which to make maximum use of her remaining talents.

This is not as easy as it sounds. The profession is becoming overcrowded, the girls lured in increasing numbers by the success of popular idols. And they are an ambitious crowd, prepared to submit to practically any indignity for the sake of professional advancement. Miss Jones could tell you stories . . . She watches these developments with quiet unease, knowing that her own survival depends on a lowering of standards, a willingness to take on work that a year ago she would have regarded as embarrassing or demeaning. Though she will only rarely bring herself to admit it, the process has already begun. Miss Jones submits uncomplainingly to these tribulations – she is a good-humoured girl who never ceases to thank providence for the stroke of fate that raised her from the typing pool – yet beneath the self-assurance ('see you *soon*,' she will enjoin as she leaves the party) her future is not an enviable one. Three years will see her in a massage parlour. Or worse.

D.J.T.

Cara & Nick

The graduates of an Oxford college can expect to be invited to their first Gaudy seven years after they have taken their degrees. It's a curious occasion: too soon, perhaps, for the many wounds of undergraduate life (the failed love affairs, the disastrous dropped catches, the trails of dried vomit) to have healed fully, but long enough for some people to have made successes of their post-university careers. Some go to meet old friends and laugh at how fat they have become, but for most, it's an irresistible opportunity to show off.

As Cara Yelland glances around the room, squinting to identify every sign of decay in the faces and frames of her peers, a tiny sigh creeps almost imperceptibly from her lips. Is it relief? Satisfaction? Or just mild boredom? In fact it's none of these. That minute emission of carbon dioxide (plus particles of a really excellent leek and foie gras terrine consumed earlier at lunch) is a signal that Cara is recharging her sincerity circuits, and is about to switch effortlessly into Brag Mode.

They may be twenty-eight, or at a pinch twenty-nine, but those seven years have clearly been stressful ones for the old crew, none of whom Cara immediately recognises. Many a luxuriant head of hair appears to have been eroded by the elements, while the few girls present are noticeably more womanly in proportion, sheepish hosts of what their

mothers would unapologetically label 'child-bearing hips'. Only Cara, who remains lithe and untainted by childbirth, has retained her youthful mien, to which she has added an ever-expanding repertoire of girlish tics and flirtatious mannerisms. But then Cara is an actress, and a successful one: she alone of her contemporaries has been able to draw strength from the unimpeachable life force of pure vanity.

She did act at Oxford, but then so did everyone else, most of them very badly and not just on the stage. Not that this mattered much at the time, for although the actors took themselves very seriously, no one else did. Cara, though, was different. Though no more gifted than anyone else, she was pretty, feminine and possessed of a fierce intelligence – to the extent that she always knew when to hide it. She therefore concentrated on looking adorable first and acting second, a tactic that worked well onstage and brilliantly in auditions. It certainly worked three days into her university career, when she was introduced to Nick Scarf in the King's Arms. Scarf was a second-year English undergraduate, vaguely handsome and a skilled apparatchik in the power structure of student drama. Cara was one of seven girls (the others dowdy, unconfident) reluctantly allowed into a previously all-male college by a Senior Common Room anxious to appear up-to-date. She and Nick wasted little time with the preliminaries, and it was soon generally agreed that they made a good-looking couple.

Their affair prospered, on and off, for two years, during which Scarf directed her as a pouting, flirtatious Desdemona and a flirtatious, pouting Hedda Gabler. They also acted together in a number of productions, and their excellent parties secured him the Presidency of OUDS for one glorious term. After his finals it seemed only natural that Scarf should 'go pro', and was immediately offered six months in Inverness rep – 'a vital learning experience', as he told everyone who asked and many people who didn't. The pair agreed to split for the sake of his career. Within two weeks Cara had become deeply involved with one of the many film-mad American postgraduates who were trying to raise unimaginable amounts of money for 'movies' about Oxford life. Again she had chosen well: her new boyfriend found a backer and made the film, with Cara (flirting, poutatious) in the lead role.

Seven years later, after a fruitful spell with one of the subsidised theatre companies (for thespian credibility) and a number of terrible films (for bucketloads of money), she has become a considerable actress, or at least quite a well-known one. She lives in Italy now, with her boyfriend, an even more famous actor than her last boyfriend. So it is with some slight and intangible sense of injustice that Nick Scarf, unnoticed, now observes her from the other side of the room. He has recently returned from another six months with Inverness rep and is currently unoccupied, although he is up for a part as a psychopath in a TV detective series. (Unknown to him, the role has been changed that morning from a thirty-two-year-old dentist to a fifty-year-old plastic surgeon.) His most visible piece of work so far – as a dashing hero in a rock video for a crypto-lesbian singer-songwriter – was four years ago. His mortgage payments are two months overdue.

Cara holds court. Most of the merchant bankers and stockbrokers chuckling indulgently at her RSC anecdotes were desperately in love with her seven or eight years ago, at least until they met their future wives at someone's twenty-first. As one of them asks if she has met Isabelle Huppert, Cara notices Nick, who is discussing the far north of Scotland with some rather less gripped contemporaries. Physically he has changed little. Still vaguely handsome, although his features are beginning to coarsen, he appears as yet undefeated by his years of disappointment. Cara tries desperately not to stare.

They talk. Cara is fine. Nick, too, is fine. Cara's work is going fine, just fine. Nick's, if anything, is even finer.

Having breathed only intermittently during this conversation, they both find themselves exhaling rather forceably on returning to their previous audiences. Nick reflects on the tyranny of age: he has frequently been assured that thirty is still young for an actor – but has he thought of teaching drama? Cara, on the other hand, decides that it may be an opportune moment to flee, brought low by a strategic sore throat. She departs in a suitably decorative fashion.

It is a scene, of course, that they will both practise again and again – Nick in plays in Kettering and Cork (and eventually to his impatient students), Cara in several well-regarded subtitled films. Each will ponder on it and discuss it with intimates, although as the faintly risible bathos of the experience recedes, and a more dramatically acceptable picture emerges, they will begin to look back on the day, and indeed their whole undergraduate affair, with a certain nostalgic indulgence. They won't remember what they have already forgotten: that they never loved each other in the first place.

M.B.

Mr Hart

In conversation and in print, Mr Hart is usually described as a Fearless Investigative Journalist. Quite why he should have attracted these adjectives is a mystery, as Mr Hart has not, during the course of his professional career, displayed any conspicuous bravery. Neither has his pursuit of information been particularly exhaustive. However, he is a man of considerable repute and even his critics – of whom there are a fair number – find it convenient to acknowledge that he is at once Fearless, Investigative and a Journalist.

Twenty years have elapsed since Mr Hart left his native land for London with the ambition of 'getting into the print', but he still gives the appearance of a man only recently arrived in England. Curiously, this impression stems not so much from his clothing or his accent – both decently moderated by now – but from an apparent unfamiliarity with milieu. People who do not know him well are sometimes amused by Mr Hart's difficulties with restaurant menus, public transport or bank opening hours, and his habit of remarking that 'it' – the food, the beer or the availability of taxis – is 'all very different' back home. By birth, Mr Hart is an Australian.

Mr Hart has never made any secret of these origins, which from a journalistic point of view are entirely advantageous: in fact he has long been conscious that his mildly un-English air is one of his chief professional assets. The advantage is less that of novelty – Mr Hart rather disapproves of what he calls 'the stage Australian' – than perspective. In his role as a television reporter Mr Hart occasionally has harsh things to imply about his adoptive country, and harsh questions to ask of some of its administrators. An Englishman who voiced these objections might sound accusing or even minatory. In contrast, there is an innocence, an ingenuousness almost, about Mr Hart's enquiries which tends to redeem them from the charge of simple prurience.

If Mr Hart himself is a Fearless Investigative Journalist, his television programmes are invariably advertised as 'compulsive' or even 'harrowing'. The description is accurate. Mr Hart's public appearances, which tend to take place three or four times a year, usually on the commercial channels, are intensely harrowing. They deal, it should be said, with those sections of society that are not generally allowed any platform for their grievances: with the destitute, the socially disadvantaged, the elderly and the frail. Their focus is as much international as domestic. Mr Hart is equally at home examining the iniquities of child labour in the Far East or revealing the deficiencies of public health care in an English borough. He is fond of reminding his audience that injustice knows no boundaries.

Mr Hart's technique as an interviewer – and the majority of his work consists of lengthy, unedited conversation – is extremely simple. He approaches his encounters without obvious preconception. The subject might be a potential victim or a potential victimiser, but in both cases Mr Hart's response is the same. Rather than hectoring, cajoling or imploring, he merely allows his guests to talk. The result is seldom less than gratifying. Audiences of Mr Hart's documentaries have grown used to the sight of venal bureaucrats betraying themselves and the injured

demonstrating the extent of their hurt. Even then, con-
fronted with self-abasing guilt or wounded innocence, Mr
Hart rarely administers a rebuke: he is aware that at these
times his pained silence may seem more eloquent than
outright condemnation. Such methods have the additional
advantage of conferring on him a reputation for 'honesty',
'integrity' and 'impartiality'.

In earlier life Mr Hart was by no means as celebrated as
he has since become. In fact, during his first days in London
he was remarkably obscure. It is not generally known, for
instance, that he began his career as a literary critic on
the *New Statesman*. Yet even at this early stage he was
conscious of being blessed with considerable advantages.
He was young, he was ambitious and (the 1960s had only
recently come to a close) he was left-wing. Moreover, his
position as one who had witnessed at first hand the passing
of a faded Imperial power – Mr Hart has strong views
on the subject of Her Majesty, the Governor General
and the prospect of an Australian republic – supposedly
qualified him to comment on a more contemporary colo-
nial struggle. Vietnam, it is safe to say, made Mr Hart's
name. By great good fortune he happened to be in Saigon
immediately before the last airlifts. His despatches, published in a liberal English newspaper and immortalised
in a celebrated television documentary, were urgent yet
dignified, anti-American, perhaps, in their implication, yet
undeniably objective. On the morning after the screening
of *Vietnam: the Final Chapter* Mr Hart woke up to find
himself famous.

It would not be true to say that Mr Hart was made
uneasy by this celebrity, by the books which he was
compelled to write and the editorials written about him
in popular newspapers, but it would be true to say that
he experienced a momentary pang of uncertainty. He was
annoyed – he could not have been surprised – by the attacks

made on him in the right-wing press, but these, he reasoned, were of little moment. More troubling, perhaps, were the stirrings of a firmly developed conscience. Mr Hart was keenly aware that he had come late to Cambodia, that his chief contribution to this sink of human suffering had been to make money from it. He resolved that his future projects should have some practical value, that they should – as he put in an interview – 'bring human beings closer together'.

Humanity being markedly fissiparous at the time, a suitable vehicle for these energies took some time to present itself. But Mr Hart kept at it. The idea of visiting Eastern Europe was not, as it happened, his own – the suggestion came from his publisher – but he seized on it with enthusiasm. He had in any case long taken an interest in the Soviet Union and its satellites, feeling them to be misrepresented, their people and institutions unjustly reviled by a Western establishment overly fond of contrasting its own 'democracy' with the supposed tyranny of the Eastern bloc. Mr Hart's visit was an unqualified success. He discovered, to his surprise, that his television cameramen were allowed almost unlimited access to desirable locations, or at the very least plausible explanations as to why such access could not be permitted. Through his contacts with senior British politicians he was enabled to interview a number of leading national figures. He knew even Brezhnev. The resultant documentary, titled *Whose Free World?* brought together a number of stark but compelling images: baleful dissidents juxtaposed with grinning party bosses, a revealing interview with a group of wide-eyed Russian airmen, a recreation of life in a Soviet labour camp. At the same time, cunningly inserted into the narrative, came images from the West – Yorkshire miners emerging from their pit shafts, defence chiefs in conference. Most memorable of all, perhaps, was Mr Hart's closing summary in which he invited the viewer to consider the gap between Western 'freedom' and Eastern 'tyranny', as revealed in these scenes, and draw his own conclusions. It was, even Mr Hart's critics agreed, a bravura performance.

In subsequent televised discussions of the programme and the newspaper articles written to accompany it, Mr Hart was called upon to deny several mischievious allegations. Chief among them was the suggestion that he was merely an apologist, albeit a very subtle one, for the Soviet regime. He did so strenuously, yet with ease. He had come not to pronounce, he informed his detractors, but to observe; not to judge but to record. His motive was to foster harmony, not to promote dissension. His only regret was that in his enthusiasm he might have overreached himself. Such refutations were convincing, not least to Mr Hart. It was noticeable, however, that in later assignments the subject of East–West relations was not one on which he cared to animadvert. He declined an invitation to interview Sakharov. In any case, the early 1980s was a time of far-flung commitments elsewhere on the globe. He covered the Falklands campaign with commendable scrupulousness (a memorable interview with captured Argentine conscripts) and, mindful of his roots, superintended a moving account of the eviction of a tribe of Aborigines from their homelands in the Northern Territories.

In his late forties, and with a decade or two of professional life before him, Mr Hart is still a widely regarded figure. He is frequently the subject of a newspaper comment, though regrettably this coverage now has a tendency to focus on an increasingly complex personal life (Mr Hart is much married and, predictably, much divorced). In recent years, however, he has tended to confine himself to matters of more domestic interest and though he still ventures abroad at regular intervals, the issues to which he likes to draw attention generally have a social rather than a political focus. Taxed with this apparent shift in perspective, Mr Hart is characteristically blunt, pointing out that the iniquities 'in our own back yard', the Embankment down-and-outs and the harassed pensioners, deserve as much attention as the victims of more remote indignities. It is a matter of regret to him that the articles he wrote some years ago about Mr Honecker and President Ceauşescu have recently been reprinted – and that they have been reprinted in journals other than those in which they first appeared. Publicly he can be heard deploring the habit of unfriendly pundits to 'take things out of context'. Mr Hart is currently much exercised by the problem of the Poll Tax. By contrast he is unaccountably silent on the subject of the East German elections. But he is still very left-wing. And he is still, without question, a Fearless Investigative Journalist.

D.J.T.

Des Stokes

Des sits and stares out of the window. Inspiration has temporarily deserted him. 'My wife's so fat,' he finally writes. The trouble is that he does not know how fat. It's clear that the spouse in question (a purely theoretical one, as Des is unmarried) should be fairly ample of proportion, if not a wobblebottom of the first order, but the appropriate simile remains tantalisingly out of reach. On the other side of the street, a small boy wanders past, idly picking his nose.

The issue of nonexistent wives' corpulence is not a trivial one, as Des is a comedy writer. Each day he sits at his word processor, surrounded by tabloid newspapers, and writes jokes. Not all his jokes are, of course, funny. Not many are, in fact. But comedy is a curious business, in which actual humour often has only a minor part to play. Fortunately, Des has diligently fostered the impression that he is 'a bit of a wag', which in the end has proved more useful than the merit (if any) of his material.

A wag he may be, but Des is not a wealthy wag. At twenty-six, his student days long past, he still inhabits a strange netherworld of postadolescent squalor, as one of four vaguely disappointed men sharing a large, inadequately heated semi-detached Victorian house in a distant suburb of North London. Surrounded by fading

lino and milk cartons of uncertain age, he is appallingly homesick.

This, though, Des finds surprising, as he never much liked home either. And it is not as though he has been deprived of his mother's disastrous cooking or his younger brother's random sexual triumphs for three weeks or even three months: it is over three years since he moved down from Blackburn. But now, as he sits contemplating matrons of no small girth, he feels lonelier and more isolated than he ever thought possible.

At the time, of course, the migration made much sense. Out of work and with little obvious aptitude for anything other than watching daytime game shows, he had started sending jokes into Radio 2's 'top-rated humour half-hour' (© *Radio Times*), *The Roy Gums Show*. Few radio or television programmes use much (if any) material that has not been commissioned beforehand, but to his surprise many of his jokes were accepted. The producer, a kindly character in avuncular middle age, encouraged him. Borrowing £500 from his mother, Des ventured to 'the smoke' (a favoured phrase) in search of cash, stardom and highly publicised relationships with unreasonably tall black girls.

And indeed he started well. Gravitating to BBC Radio's Light Entertainment department (through which many a hopeful, and indeed hopeless, young jokesmith has passed over the decades), he was immediately commissioned for a minute a week on a well-known Radio 4 satire show. This was unheard of for an unknown, but Des had a unique advantage: he was the son of the late Syd Stokes, the comedy writer known throughout the jokes business as 'the man who never smiles'. Syd, whose exploits were still being tediously recounted by other writers ten years after his suicide, had never been seen to show any manifestation of amusement (beyond the occasional raised eyebrow) throughout his long and fruitful career. With the doom-laden words 'Here's a funny one', he would hand another selection of timeless comic gems to his producer and silently withdraw. Syd Stokes didn't say much, but what he did say was rarely ignored. When he told you that something you had done was 'too funny', you stopped to take notice.

It was quite a pedigree, and Des was not foolish enough to turn down anything as prestigious as a one-minute commission on *What, No Punchline?*. There were problems, though. Such a commission was highly prized amongst the regular writers on the programme, many of whom had had to battle for months or years to get it. This parvenu, with his famous father and homely Lancastrian ways, had done nothing to merit the honour bar a few elderly mother-in-law jokes for Roy Gums. Poor Des was not welcomed into Comedy Corridor with flags and bunting. On the contrary, he was widely shunned. Though perfectly personable and, like most joke writers, entertaining in short bursts, he was deliberately excluded from all social activities (going to the BBC Club, going to the pub, going to the outrageously overpriced Indonesian restaurant down the road).

Unfortunately for Des, the world of broadcasting is primarily a social one, with the ability to make the right friends as vital a commodity as actual talent. Des could have survived without the talent – unlike his father, he wasn't especially good – but his inability to get on with the right people eventually proved calamitous. After a year on *What, No Punchline?*, his contract was not renewed. The 'alternative' style favoured by the show did not come easily to him, and his producer, an Oxford graduate who campaigned actively for the SWP, found Des's indifference to political matters hard to stomach.

This failure sent Des into a small decline. Alone and unemployed in London, without close friends or even the merest sniff of a love life (for all his finely honed chat-up technique, the black girls had so far found him far from irresistible), he seriously entertained the prospect of a humiliating return home. Indeed he vanished from sight for months – so long that even the gagwriters who had spurned him at the BBC wondered what had happened to him. When he at last re-emerged, it was with news of regular if unexotic employment – a little copywriting for a small and hard-up advertising agency, plus some jokewriting for a telephone 'gagline'. If he had lost some of his old bounce, his acquaintances failed to notice it.

Since then he has progressed slowly, taking other equally prosaic jobs when radio and TV work has eluded him. Indeed, how he manages to find these jobs – and keep them – has become of enduring interest to his fellow jokewriters. Now seen only rarely at BBC Radio (to hand in his one-liners for the *Gums Show*), he has become a reclusive, almost ascetic figure. Though amiable enough when cornered (he is, after all, 'a bit of a wag'), he appears never to have forgiven his contemporaries' early hostility.

Suddenly, though, his name has begun to show up on the end credits of a few slightly downmarket TV shows. If not as prestigious as some of the more fashionable BBC2 sketch programmes, *The Doug Dunstable Show* nevertheless pays substantially better than radio – and it's noticed by many more people. For Des may not be especially talented, but he is a keen student of the rules of comedy. He talks constantly of 'tags' and 'toppers', of 'gag counts' and 'reveals'. He knows how a joke should work, and that, for Doug Dunstable, is what's required. The show is a success, and so, it seems, is Des. His Lancastrian accent is more pronounced than ever before.

Des continues to stare out of the window. Then, changing tack a little, he comes up with an idea. 'My wife's so thin,' he writes, 'that when she drinks tomato juice she looks like a thermometer.' No, he decides, tearing it up. It's too funny.

M.B.

Mr Slattery

'A nice quiet little place this is,' Mr Slattery will say with an expansive gesture around the barroom, or, 'We do our best to make people feel at home here.' On the strength of these remarks and a rather obvious familiarity with his surroundings occasional callers at the Crown often assume that Mr Slattery has something to do with its management, that he is the landlord or possibly even a visiting representative from the brewery. This is not in fact the case. Despite his faint proprietorial air and the marked neatness of his dress, Mr Slattery is no more than an ordinary member of what it amuses him to call 'the drinking classes'.

Mr Slattery does not exactly live in the Crown – just off the High Street, Jas. Dickinson prop., coaches by appointment – but he is perhaps the nearest thing to an habitué that the place possesses. Though barely into his forties he has been coming here for as long as anyone can remember: even the head barmaid, herself a ten-year veteran, cannot recall a time when he failed to occupy his customary stool at the far end of the lounge bar or stand in front of the flaring gas fire with his head half-cocked, listening to the town hall clock striking the hour. To longevity is added conspicuous regularity. It is rare for him to miss an evening, even at weekends or on public

holidays, and if he can 'square it with the boss' – Mr Slattery works as the local representative of an insurance company – he has been known to turn up at lunchtime. At a rough computation, perhaps a third of his waking life is spent in this way.

Quite why Mr Slattery should have selected this particular haunt as a venue for his leisure hours is a mystery, as the Crown possesses few of the amenities traditionally associated with public houses. It is, for instance, dimly lit; it supplies little in the way of food; and its population – office workers on their way home, silent lorry drivers, lost cyclists – is largely transient. However, it is a fact that Mr Slattery regards the Crown with an affection bordering on veneration. He has been known to refer to it, not entirely jocosely, as 'my second hearth' or even, in very emotional moments, as 'the dear old place'. This air of deep, personal attachment is sharpened by a remarkable memory for the pub's recent history and personnel. Mr Slattery's powers of recall are not generally impressive, and he would be hard put to tell you the name of the present foreign secretary, but he can remember 'as if it was yesterday' the time when the beer pump failed, the amount raised in the Christmas charity collection and the last occasion on which a drunk was thrown out (a very long time ago, that). When given the opportunity, he will chaff 'mine host' – Mr Slattery's name for the landlord – on his own fallibility in these areas.

In keeping with his status as a regular, Mr Slattery enjoys various privileges that would not be accorded to the Crown's more casual visitors. He has his own stool and his own tankard, and is allowed on occasion to go behind the bar to serve his own drinks. Needless to say his relations with the bar staff are outwardly of the most cordial sort. He calls them by their Christian names, frequently stands them drinks and listens with interest to the details of their domestic lives. On busy nights – Saturdays, or when the town's football team has a midweek game – he will often 'make himself useful', as he puts it, by collecting used glasses or even – the Crown is chronically understaffed – assisting at the bar himself. It must be said that Mr Slattery is not markedly adept at serving beer and has a habit of miscalculating change, but his occasional deficiencies are redeemed by constant good humour. For their part the staff supply him with glasses of port 'on the house' and bring him small bowls of peanuts and potato crisps for his private consumption. Mr Slattery enjoys these tokens of esteem, regarding them as essential components in the manufacture of what he calls 'a nice friendly atmosphere'.

Some people come to public houses to drink, others to eat, play darts or listen to the jukebox. Mr Slattery, it is safe to say, comes for conversation. He is not much of a drinker, seldom consuming three or four half-pints of bitter in the course of an evening, and for the Crown to invest in an electronic games machine would be to guarantee his departure, but he relishes what he calls 'a bit of a natter' or 'a good old clickety-clack'. Mr Slattery's pursuit of this quarry is characterised by a disinterestedness which verges on humility. He realises, mark you, that his fellow drinkers might not wish to be bothered by the attentions of 'yours truly' or 'your humble servant' – Mr Slattery has a facetious streak and invariably introduces himself in this way – and he is at pains to defer to the interests or prejudices of his targets. Should you be engaged on a newspaper crossword he will be happy to assist you in your speculations, even to the extent of soliciting a dictionary from the landlord. Should you happen to be discussing some sporting event or political question of the day, he will delight in adding his own modest voice to the discussion. Mr Slattery's interventions, it must be said, are distinguished by impressive courtesy, and no matter how tenacious or inflammatory your views he will always hear you out before expressing his own. These tend to be uncontroversial. Mr Slattery is a Conservative by instinct and an anti-European by inclination, but he can usually be persuaded to agree that Labour 'ought to be given a chance', or that the Channel Tunnel 'has something to be said for it'. Such a willingness to please is rare among public house habitúes. The air of tolerant emollience which Mr Slattery manages to bring to the occasional squabble or loud-voiced disagreement provides an edifying spectacle.

Public opinion at the Crown is divided about Mr Slattery. He is generally held to be a bit of a bore, but then this is an environment particularly suited to the nurture of bores and there are worse than Mr Slattery. According to long-established convention he ought to be the victim of profound domestic discontent, a harassed escapee from marital thraldom, yet in contrast to the majority of the clientele, the morose husbands and surly adulterers, Mr Slattery is happy to confess to the existence of a wife and two children and to discuss them with considerable enthusiasm. He is an unfailingly cheerful little man, although it is noticeable, perhaps, that his cheerfulness recedes rather than appreciates as the evening wears on. It is also noticeable that his most fervent conversations tend to be conducted with casual migrants to the pub rather than the longer term associates of the lounge bar.

There are, it should be said, occasional jokes made about Mr Slattery's obsession with his chosen milieu. He is, for example, supposed to have been unreasonably agitated by the recent extension to the licensing hours on the grounds that it reduced proportionately his opportunities. There have also been unkind remarks about camp beds. Yet it cannot be denied, in his defence, that the Crown has no more passionate advocate. Should you venture by chance into 'the dear old place' you can be certain of a warm welcome from Mr Slattery. He will introduce you to the landlord, make sure that you get a seat by the fire, advise you on the selection of drinks (for one who drinks so sparingly he is oddly knowledgeable about beer) and do his best to make you feel at home. However, the chances are that you will not stay very long. After all, being agreed with is seldom an effective stimulus to conversation. There is also the disadvantage that the place is generally pretty empty. The landlord, to do him justice, is aware of this failing. In fact he has almost made up his mind to install a Space Invaders machine.

D.J.T.

Aimee

It was on an obscure early morning children's TV programme that Aimee first saw Froth. The song, a negli-
gible but modish ditty, she scarcely noticed. The group's
incompetent attempts at miming, she registered not at
all. But their faces, their hair, their bodies, their dimply
smiles . . .

They were simply too pretty for words. Jake, the lead
singer: limpid eyes, short dark hair, flawless skin, with a
voice like Diana Ross on helium. Sam, the bassist: beautiful
lips, short fair hair, a perfect bottom, and capable of holding
his guitar the right way round. Even Nick, the fat boy
drummer, wasn't a complete write-off. Aimee watched,
enthralled, and spent the rest of the weekend sighing.

Naturally no one had heard of Froth. Aimee told Dawn
and Charlene at the first opportunity, but they were still
following the Trouser brothers, Mark and John. So, in
theory, was Aimee – at least, if you considered the fifty-
two posters of the Trousers on her wall as admissible
evidence. But as pictures of Froth laughing, horsing about
and wearing slightly too much make-up began to insinu-
ate themselves into the pages of *Smash Hits*, so Aimee
changed her allegiance. She became one of the very first
Frothettes.

This involved a radical change of lifestyle. Having left

school the previous summer, her departure hastened by her entirely unexpected acquisition of a GCSE (which rendered her 'qualified'), Aimee had quickly found a job in a local bakery. To her surprise, many of her friends had decided to stay on at school, mainly because it would afford more time in which to pursue Mark and John Trouser. These two twenty-year-olds, who had had a gigantic pan-European hit the previous year with 'So Butch', were recording their second album at a secret location – which the girls, thanks to a friendly chauffeur, soon identified as a studio in an adjoining London suburb. For hour upon hour they would stand outside the building, waiting apparently for ever in the hope of catching even the faintest glimpse of the boys' unnaturally perfect bone structures. In the process they got to know the boys' manager, producer and minders, not to mention Mark's girlfriend Shelley and John's 'old chum' Gavin. When the boys finally left for the evening, the girls would leap into Dawn's mother's Fiesta and pursue them to their 'secret hideaway' – a heavily guarded flat in Fulham. There they would stay for a few more hours, until one of the minders playfully directed a water cannon at them or inadvertently unleashed the guard dogs.

As Aimee's obsession grew, so did her collection of full-colour Trouser posters, until those four alien cheekbones masked every trace of the undistinguished wallpaper that had previously characterised her room. Not that it was a very large room – Aimee's mother's council flat was not, by any standards, one of Catford's more desirable properties – but in covering the ceiling as well, Aimee had not stinted in her admiration of the unearthly brothers. Her worship had not even faltered during the press revelations of payola, casting couches and curiously shaped gardening implements.

But where the cream of the world's press had failed to divert her attention, Froth succeeded. As *Smash Hits* and

Just Seventeen picked up on the new young group, Aimee's beloved Trouser posters gradually disappeared from sight, while Jake, Sam and even chubby Nick found themselves promoted to the most prestigious of vantage points – above Aimee's teddy-bedecked pillow. Instead of following the Trousers around London, Aimee began to spend her free time in pursuit of Froth.

By coincidence it was at about this time that the Trouser phenomenon began to lose momentum. Their sixth single, 'Shave Me', barely scraped the top ten, and exited the charts as though pursued by a bear. Even Dawn and Charlene were asking each other and themselves whether the aubergine story might have been true after all, and the Trouser brothers began saying Yes to press interviews, after months of unequivocal Nos.

But Aimee was no longer interested. As she sold a rather overcrusty bloomer to Mrs Ferris, she was expending the vast majority of her mental energies on something infinitely more taxing: trying to work out how she could meet Sam. Others preferred Jake, the poor fools, but Sam . . . She didn't seriously imagine that he would fall in love with her, but you never knew . . .

And so she continued to follow Froth, from company headquarters to studio, from studio to management offices, from management offices to their parents' homes. Dawn joined her; Charlene stayed with the Trousers. Aimee was first at the barricades erected by an irritated local constabulary, she wore the clothes Sam said he liked girls to wear in his exclusive *Number One* interview, she even wore make-up, which she knew didn't suit her. Sam began to acknowledge her; he even occasionally chatted to her and Dawn late at night, outside the studio. But then he was always whisked off, just as the Trousers had been, just as all the others had been.

At eighteen, Aimee has yet to have a boyfriend – like

Dawn, Charlene and the rest, she would argue that she hasn't time for 'all that'. (Charlene is thought to have had one once, but the details are sketchy.) Although all are seventeen or eighteen, none of the three looks their age, or really feels it. And none of them has any money. When at home (Aimee gets on well with her mother) she watches television, or plays tapes in her bedroom, while devouring all known printed matter dedicated to her idols. Ask her and she'll tell you that she knows it's silly, that she always realised that she never had a chance with Sam (who is in fact sleeping with his manager), and that the music's rubbish, really. But she'll also tell you that she's happy. Since she started following pop stars around, she's made more and better friends than she ever had as a shy, plain, inarticulate schoolgirl. The future, she knows, is not especially exciting, but the present is fun. And it's better, she'd argue, than getting pregnant and married, as one or two of the school's denser pupils have since done.

Now if only she could get to meet Jake . . .

M.B.

Mrs D'Souza

It was at the funeral of an elderly friend, an event attended by a great many other elderly ladies and held in a cavernous church off the Harrow Road, that Mrs D'Souza first heard the voice of God. Although she had read a proportion of that vast literature which deals with such a contingency, nothing in Mrs D'Souza's experience had served to prepare her for this unexpected visitation. For, as she was later to admit, it had few of the lineaments traditionally associated with a spiritual summons. No angel emerged above the catafalque of her late acquaintance and moved mysteriously to greet her. No flash of otherworldly light came suddenly to disturb the muttered obsequies of a bowed congregation. Subsequently, in one of the countless confidences, discussions and speculations which were henceforth to dominate Mrs D'Souza's existence, she was only able to describe it in terms of a lightening of atmosphere, a ghostly chiaroscuro of lighted shade, in which a single voice could be heard to speak distinctly. 'I am God,' it said simply. 'I am God.' Shaken, quivering with strange, vibrant emotions, Mrs D'Souza walked out of the church to find her life disagreeably transformed.

At first Mrs D'Souza was inclined to dismiss such evidence as there was of divine intervention. An intelligent, unfailingly rational woman in her late sixties, in whom the

activities of the late Mr D'Souza had done no more than inculcate a mild cynicism, she at first ascribed the voice to an overexcitement with scene. Although this explanation was later amended to 'nerves' and later still to a light-headedness induced by two pre-service sherries, Mrs D'Souza was keenly conscious of its inadequacy; a feeling reinforced on the occasions when the voice returned. It came early one morning in the week following the funeral, causing Mrs D'Souza to drop a tray and smash three antique Dresden cups. It came again, three evenings later, causing Mrs D'Souza to put down the fan of playing cards ranged neatly between her fingers and weep with anxiety. By the end of the third week, when the voice had settled into a routine of appearing briefly in the small hours and then later, though not invariably, around teatime, Mrs D'Souza had, not unreasonably, conceived that something should be done.

This 'something', this 'finding some rational explanation for it all', as Mrs D'Souza put it in the many conversations which began at about this time, admitted no easy solution. The past, though combed for portents and allusions, suggested no event to which it could be safely ascribed. Mrs D'Souza had not earlier on in her life been one of those girls who sit in the dark holding hands or, a little later, go in for ghost stories or Ouija boards. She had once, it is true, attended a seance, but the sight of a medium conjuring up ectoplasm from what was patently a hunk of butter muslin did nothing but incite her disgust. Then there was the fact that the voice relayed no obvious threat. It did not present her with a catalogue of past depravities or hint at future embarrassment. It simply said that it was God. The professional advice which Mrs D'Souza eventually sought offered scant consolation. Her local vicar, a young man bored by the neuroses of his predominantly elderly and female congregation, diffidently suggested prayer. Her doctor, an older man who had known Mrs D'Souza's husband, prescribed rest, sedatives and a change of air. The voice continued.

Subsequently, Mrs D'Souza noted a change in this unlooked-for manifestation. She became aware, gradually, that there was not one voice but several and that their tone, singly and collectively, was increasingly unpleasant. In high-pitched, childlike tones, in low, guttural grunts, in mellifluous cadences which reminded her of a long-dead friend, she found herself accused of a variety of shocking transgressions: of adultery, of indifference to her late husband, of frigidity, child molestation (Mrs D'Souza was, as it happened, childless but the voice did not specify) and drug-taking. This, perhaps, Mrs D'Souza could have borne. She was of a stoical disposition and the customary upheavals of domestic life – marriage, removal, death – had left her largely unmoved. What she could not tolerate was the increasingly public nature of these pronouncements. Were she to board a bus, a reasonable male tone, apparently coming from the seat beside her, would depose that she was a riotous pervert. Were she to venture into Harrods to shop, a swirl of voices would fly down from the grocery counter to suggest that she had wilfully hastened her sister's death. On the day on which Mrs D'Souza's bridge partner appeared to accuse her of seducing the late Earl of Stockton in the shrubbery at Chequers, Mrs D'Souza retired into her neat little service flat in Kensington Church Street and would not come out.

Lodged in this self-imposed sequestration, Mrs D'Souza remains a figure of some resilience. In her youth she had been known as a 'strong-minded woman' and the events of the past year have done little to undermine her faith in her own rectitude. At sixty-eight, tall, dark-haired and soberly dressed – in fact bearing a distinct resemblance to Whistler's portrait of his mother – she is still a dominating force in the assemblages of friends which periodically take place in her flat. Even in her hour of tribulation Mrs D'Souza is a zealous hostess. Her friends repay this kindness by talking of her 'bravery' and her 'determination', by bringing to her acquaintances who have suffered (and triumphed over) similar experiences and by offering her small packets of groceries. The same friends, it should be said, find her greatly altered, 'rather strange', or even – this from a younger woman who does not know Mrs D'Souza well – 'sinister'.

The situation is complicated by the fact that Mrs D'Souza seems strangely unaware of the extent of her obsession, or of the gradual fragmentation to which her life is now subject. At first a collection of doctors, psychiatrists and other specialists came fairly regularly to visit her. Lately these visits have ceased. There was nothing demonstrably wrong with Mrs D'Souza: as a result she found these incursions unwelcome and put a stop to them. Periodically some new theory arises briefly to awaken her interest – cosmic rays, planetary disturbance and so forth – but none is capable of providing more than a fleeting explanation. The worst of it is that the role played by the voices, at first unsettling, then threatening, is now verging on the consolatory. Despite the calumnies and the outrageous suggestions, Mrs D'Souza would probably admit that the happiest part of her day is spent in monitoring these ghostly monologues and recording them in a series of exercise books. Much of her leisure time is taken up in reading and rereading the contents of this small but burgeoning library. It is, after all, as she never tires of reminding her friends, the voice of God. Meanwhile, the range of Mrs D'Souza's acquaintance has begun rapidly to diminish and may soon disappear altogether. The likelihood of her ever setting foot outside her flat again or living what might be described as a normal life is remote.

D.J.T.

Giles Watkyn

In 1381, Sir Thomas Watkynne played his part in the quelling of the Peasants' Rebellion, when he absent-mindedly lent someone the knife that killed Wat Tyler. In 1685, after the Monmouth Revolt, Sir Edward Watkyn MP pointedly criticised Judge Jeffreys for being too liberal, and called for 'a firm hand'. And in 1819 the Hon Percy Watkyn, second son of the second Marquess and a callow second lieutenant in the cavalry, witnessed the consequences of his actions as he jovially shouted 'Charge!' at the Peterloo Massacre. It was against this background that in 1958, at the age of twenty-one, Giles Watkyn became a Marxist.

It was not a hard decision to make. Intellectually, the strictures of ideology appealed to him. A fleeting glance out of his window overlooking Tom Quad was enough to persuade him of the appallingly random, even messy nature of modern life, and yet here was a system of thought that not only agreed that it should be cleared up, but gave explicit instructions on how to do it. The practicalities of socialist revolution could, of course, be left to those best qualified to carry them out – the trades unionists, the community leaders and generally everybody under the yoke of capitalist oppression. But Giles would do what they couldn't do – he would think about it, and read about it, and write about it.

And so, after university, he poured a tiny fraction of his considerable inheritance (the more demotically spelt Watkin's Bank was run by his uncle and two cousins) into a small but lively magazine that, after four irregularly published issues, had appealed with some desperation for funds. Having arrived as benefactor, Giles stayed to become first contributor, briefly administrator and, from 1963, chairman of the Editorial Committee that met once a fortnight. *Left*, over the next twenty years, published many of the world's most revered Marxist dialecticians, several of whom took unpaid but enthusiastic part in forming editorial policy: Professor Fred Phillipson (Editorial Committee 1969–82), Dr George Shearer (EC 1974–81) and even the notorious Bennite MP Reg Stench (EC 1978–83) were but three of the participants. The journal's long, serious, detailed and all but incomprehensible articles unwound every strand of Marxist thought, and applied them to the events of the day, or more accurately (thanks to strict publishing deadlines) the previous year. Issues were numbered rather than dated, perfect bound and printed in a small conservative typeface. Academic respectability was the aim, and most of the founding participants enjoyed successful parallel careers, writing for the *New Statesman* or appearing on TV chat shows expounding violent revolution in quiet upper-class voices.

Giles, through all this, concentrated exclusively on *Left*. Unlike his colleagues, he was not obliged to make a living, and appeared to be without personal ambition. In 1966 he married Griselda, a younger and slightly starstruck Cambridge undergraduate who was intelligent enough to know how intelligent Giles was but not quite intelligent enough to make him look stupid. He remained in the Eaton Square house that Chief Justice Watkyn had commissioned two centuries before, and there they brought up two children, James and Henrietta. Much of the time he worked at home, apparently on a projected history of Albania, in a study whose clutter contrasted curiously with the formal sparseness of the rest of the house. Two or three times a week he popped into the office in his man-of-the-people denim suit (freshly laundered), to potter, check that everything was going smoothly and have long earnest conversations with anyone who happened to be around.

By 1977, and his fortieth birthday, *Left* had established itself as perhaps the most prestigious and least readable publication of its type. A book publishing arm had been established to deal with longer works, and many of the magazine's stalwarts were solid figures of the socialist establishment. This left Giles to retain editorial control of the magazine, although a nominal editor was there to do the actual work. As chairman of the EC, Giles saw himself as the magazine's eminence grise, and as people naturally drifted away from the magazine, he installed others who were perhaps more in tune with his ways of doing things. But amidst all this success, widespread respectability and even, for a time, mild profitability, there were, by the end of the seventies, distinct signs that all was not well. For one thing Tim Hadfield, the magazine's editor and another of its stalwarts, was beginning to tire of Giles's interference in matters of content and style. For another, although Tim did not know it, Giles was sleeping with his wife. And then, in 1980, came the biggest blow yet: Solidarity. As the world's newspapers rang with praise for Lech Walesa and his historic stand against Soviet-backed state communism, *Left* remained oddly silent about the affair. A year after the story broke, the magazine that had provided the most eloquent critique of *les évenements* of Paris in 1968, the Kent State Massacre of 1970, and even (bullishly) the Soviet Union's invasion of Afghanistan in 1979, had uttered not a syllable. As far as *Left* appeared to be concerned, nothing of consequence had happened.

In reality, of course, the Solidarity affair had sparked off long and bitter arguments within the Editorial Committee. After nine months' solid bickering, it was tacitly agreed that nothing further would be said on the subject, at least until 'a historical perspective' could be brought to bear on events. That this compromise amounted to little more than a cop-out was swiftly noticed in academic socialist circles, and people began to gossip. One or two of the more vocal dissenters resigned from the EC (going on to write long and dreary articles in the *Guardian* about their reasons for so doing); others just lost interest and showed up in the office less and less frequently.

But if Giles's dithering about Solidarity was unfortunate – it was his personal indecision that had created the impasse – his next mistake was disastrous. After the magazine's clerical assistant had been late for a second time in a week, Giles fired her. She told a tabloid newspaper, whose idiosyncratic brand of right-wing populism liked to blame all the country's ills on 'the loony left' and 'the toffs': their joy at finding a victim who fitted both descriptions was unbounded. She had been fired, she told them, not because she was inadequate at her job, but because she had once left on her desk a magazine with a photograph of Prince Charles on the cover. Giles had seen this and completely lost his temper, tearing the magazine to shreds (that morning Tim's wife had told him that she was pregnant with his child). The paper leapt into the story with abandon, interviewing James and Henrietta at their prep schools and doorstepping Griselda for a week.

Giles hid. He had never liked the clerical assistant, whose unabashed proletarianism he found impossible to deal with (she was also keen on Mrs Thatcher). Giles was extremely keen on the working classes as a concept, but didn't invite them to dinner parties. Even Reg Stench turned out to be one of the Gloucestershire Stenches.

In despair Giles turned to an old friend, the once famous revolutionary Paraqat Ali (always mischievously spelt 'Paraquat' by the tabloids), who had spent the sixties storming barricades and generally having a good time. Introduced to the EC two years before, Paraqat now set about finding who was on Giles's side and who wasn't. He knew both, of course, but this did not prevent him setting up what he portentously called 'a commission of enquiry', with formal meetings and interviews over a period of six weeks. *Left* was held by observers to have reached 'a crisis point'. With the Labour Party also in the process of tearing itself apart in drawn-out procedural struggles, the tabloids lost interest in this smaller story; the ex-clerical assistant was paid off, and *Left* was left to get on with it.

When the talking was finally over, the Editorial Committee reconvened. Virtually all the long-serving members of the EC had resigned or asked to leave, and a new collection had been recruited, many with a strong interest in Third World affairs. To Giles's shock, Paraqat was instantly elected as chairman in his place, as a 'stopgap' while Giles took a brief 'sabbatical' to work on his history of Albania. He had been knifed.

Five years later, Giles is back in control of the magazine – Paraqat was soon offered an all too tempting job at Channel 4 – but the momentum has been lost. Circulation has fallen drastically, and the contributors are noticeably less eminent than before. Only Giles's bounty keeps it afloat, and now that he is paying for two households – Griselda and the children refuse to move out of Eaton Square – his resources are stretched for the first time. He still has custody of the denim suit, however, and continues to potter into the office a couple of times a week. The political changes throughout Europe have intellectually disarmed him – he makes no effort to lead the views of the magazine, mainly because he hasn't any cogent ones of his own – but at least Albania hasn't crumbled yet, and his keenly awaited history, recently completed, is due for publication next year. He has still to find a project to take its place.

Meanwhile the last of the Watkyns, James, has announced that he plans to join the family bank after graduation, at which point he also plans to move in with his boyfriend. Somewhere, Giles often reflects, everything has gone terribly wrong: modern life is, if anything, even messier than it was before. Perhaps a history of Cuba would be a good idea . . .

M.B.

Max

'I'm my own man,' Max will say casually, or, in more deliberate tones, 'I can look after my own interests.' His audience, the clientele of some smart, anonymous pub off Oxford Street, the after-hours drinkers in the select establishment on the Bayswater Road, may not be able to verify these claims but they can attest to their significance. They are their own men too, up to a point. Certainly Max is no one else's man: not his mother's, to whom he is no more than an occasional voice on the telephone, or his wife's, who has not seen him these past three years. No DSS office, council rating department or vehicle licensing unit has ever heard of him. No bank, building society or insurance company has registered his name on any account, policy or data base. For all practical purposes, Max might scarcely be said to exist.

Max's professional life abets this sense of chronic anonymity. In conversation he might cautiously admit to being 'a businessman', 'a small trader', or even, in more exalted moments, 'an entrepreneur', without affording the listener any hint of what it is that his business consists. The telephone number inscribed on the business card beneath his name – and it is all that is inscribed there – may or may not reach him. His personal life encompasses no distinct locale or settled habit. He might be seen in the quiet South

Kensington bistro every night for a week and then not at all. He is as much at home at a greyhound stadium in the East End as in a Chelsea drawing room, but neither the dog-track habitués or the roomful of dinner-jacketed diners will know who he is or where he comes from. In any case his dealings with them are not of a kind to encourage familiarity.

The presence in the Chelsea drawing room – at Ascot once, heaven knows how – is an indication of how far Max has come in the last few years: he is of what used to be called 'humble' origins and the Bermondsey accent, never wholly quelled, has checked more than one pouting ingénue in her stride. Not that Max regrets these wasted opportunities. He regards his customers with very faint contempt: 'Posh bitches with more money than brains. Blokes thinking they're doing the trendy thing. I wouldn't give you tuppence for the lot of them.' As Max takes no interest in the product he sells, other than as a source of profit, his attitude to the Camillas and the Jolyons is that of a sexually cold prostitute towards her clientele. Whatever the degree of social camouflage, it is, after all, only the preliminary to a business transaction. And Max, after all, is his own man.

It is a profitable business, this, what Max does for a living: vagrant, furtive and occasionally dangerous – but profitable. But then Max, a Bermondsey boy who as he puts it has 'knocked around a bit', is used to living on and off his wits. Since his mid-teens, an irregular council school education having provided him with no qualifications for or interest in bona fide employment, he has pursued a variety of more or less illegal occupations: as a runner, once, for a crooked bookmaker in the clotted streets of Poplar; selling faulty electrical 'seconds', a little later, behind cracked plate-glass windows in the Bethnal Green Road. Precarious trades, their restrictions nimbly evaded, they

have bought him, ten years on, the outward prosperity he
craves – the car, the suit, the improbably blonde girlfriends
– but without satisfying a more pronounced instinct for
permanence. A dozen of the Oxford Street habitués might
know Max by sight, and half of these might know his
name or current alias, but not one of them could claim
his friendship, or care to claim it. Even in the less than
scrupulous circles in which Max moves, the cash seldom
translates into cachet.

This lack of anything but the most cursory acquaintanceship is a pity, for Max is a convivial soul, prone,
when in funds, to stand drinks for roomfuls of comparative
strangers, envious of the lost opportunities for conversation
and friendship with the 'lads', 'mates' and 'good blokes'.
Inevitably, and to do him justice regretfully, his sexual
relationships are of the most primitive cast. Max knows
that no steady girl would stand the late hours or the queer
company: he marks it down as the price paid for a nervy
yet increasingly extravagant lifestyle. Friends would also
be an advantage in a business environment which has, in
recent years, become increasingly cutthroat. Three years
ago, two years ago even, Max worked in a marketplace
full of other small-timers like himself, ever ready to pool
information and sales tips. It was the nearest he ever came
to the Elysian blokerie that remains his idea of a good time.
But the big boys are moving in, the representatives of a
seedy corporatism to whom the Maxes of this world, with
their simple ambitions and minor affiliations, are deeply
inimical. Alone, friendless, but circumspect, Max prowls
on, uneasily conscious of fading influence in what was
always a very limited sphere.

Max is not quite unknown, of course. There is a file on
him in West End Central and many a plain-clothes detective
prepared to nod should they encounter one another in the
course of some late-night jaunt. Max is unworried by these

attentions. 'I've got nothing to hide,' he will say. 'They've got nothing they can pin on me.' For their part the police are equally uninterested in Max. He has never met anyone of the slightest importance in the course of his travels. No attempt to set him up as bait to entice larger fry or better-known suppliers would ever come to anything. Max is not aware that greater celebrity would, paradoxically, guarantee his security. For the police to keep an eye, as they do with important criminals, is itself a form of protection which Max would give a great deal to possess.

As it is, when Max's pack of cards comes tumbling down, when somebody who has hitherto tolerated his activities decides to tolerate no longer, when Max's 'manor', an increasingly hazardous domain, is colonised by the cowboys, no one will notice. Max will simply disappear – missed for a few days, perhaps, by the Oxford Street irregulars, by the furtive young men at the debutante ball, but neither mourned nor regretted. Until that time Max will remain: an elusive, ageless and slightly exhausted figure – but still, indisputably, his own man.

D.J.T.

Gordon Askew

The sobriquet 'train spotter' has long been used to describe any hobby-fixated male whose obsession leads him, by irresistible circumstance, to don a kagoule, greasy trainers and a pair of NHS spectacles (cracked). No doubt there are many genuine train spotters who note numbers in Versace suits before nipping off to lunch with Bianca Jagger, but over the years the stereotype has tended to stick.

Gordon Askew has never heard of Versace, thinks Bianca Jagger is some sort of cocktail and indeed is only dimly aware of the existence of trains. For him, the focal point of all existence is the ten-inch monitor screen that rests on his otherwise uncluttered desk; across its accompanying keyboard, the fingers of his right hand flit with surprising dexterity. Gordon is nineteen, and emits the distinctive odour of infrequently washed sweatshirts that so precisely characterises the age.

It is late at night; Gordon is grappling with a troublesome bit of code. The company for which he works, Trollsoft, operates from a converted garage in Sheffield; the offices overlook the Wooden Horse, to which he hopes soon to repair. Gordon has recently discovered real ale, and sometimes pops down after work for a few 'jars' with the 'lads' (he has already mastered the necessary jargon). But first he just has to sort out this routine . . .

GORDON ASKEW

Gordon enjoys his job. He programs games for all the most popular machines, the Turbot 400, the Guppy XB20 and the soon-to-be-superseded Whelkstall IV. Two games he has worked on, Ninja Arthropod and Starcruncher, have reached number one in the national chart, although as an employee he takes no royalty, merely what he regards as an excessively generous salary. Gordon's task is to write the machine code for the game – its fundamental workings. Others before him will have designed the game, and others after him will supply music and graphics.

Gordon's achievements are regarded by all, not least by himself, as astonishing. Until the age of thirteen he had been a startlingly unpromising child: inarticulate, cadaverous and prematurely scrofulous. Remorselessly bullied by other children, teachers, inanimate objects and large dogs, he came to accept that, through ill luck or the grim inevitability of fate, he was doomed to a life of solitary, intermittently purulent inadequacy. Puberty, which he suffered early, came as an even greater blow: the coarse black hairs that sprouted up in all the most inconvenient crannies of his body tragically failed to complement the deathly gleam of his blue-white skin.

But on his thirteenth birthday, Gordon was given a computer. His parents, ignorant of the market, had bought a remaindered 16K Megamullet, but their son's enthusiasm soon overcame the machine's obvious inadequacies. Soon he was spending most evenings quietly adhered to his joystick; his parents, who had earlier been worried that he was going to masturbate himself to death, were agreeably surprised. Within six months he was not just playing games, he was hacking into them, guided at first by the plethora of poorly written magazines devoted to the subject, and subsequently by an instinct whose sureness has never ceased to amaze him. For, as he worked out yet more ingenious ways of securing infinite lives in Hypersphere and Samurai Hamster (later sending the results into *Megamullet User* magazine), he discovered his talent: he could read machine code. History, mathematics and English may have remained opaque to him, but machine code was transparently clear.

His parents, whose early lives had been similarly tainted by shyness and lack of confidence until, by an extraordinary stroke of luck, they met each other, encouraged Gordon throughout. True, his personal relations with the rest of the human race were still tenuous at best, but by writing regularly to the magazines with the results of his researches, he was at least acknowledging that other people existed. At sixteen he began writing games of his own, which, although bereft of originality, were at least elegantly constructed. One of them was sent to Trollsoft, who noticed this and recruited him after O levels.

Gordon still lives at home; his parents, as before, let him be. Indeed, any other form of existence would be unthinkable to both parties. These days, though, he is there only infrequently. His work consumes most of his day, as he wallows happily in the sheer profusion of digits that would terrify anyone not inculcated in the mysteries of computer programming. Games, as such, no longer interest him: he plays them only when he has to. It's the simple beauty of the numbers that draws him in, the magical significance of pure data. That, and uncountable cups of coffee, keep him going for ten, sometimes twelve hours every day.

After work, though, Gordon no longer goes straight home, whether or not there are sympathetic souls to discuss programming techniques with over a quiet drink. Indeed, he has taken to visiting the Wooden Horse for long periods whether he knows anyone there or not. It's not the real ale that particularly attracts him – it's the occasional presence there of Martin, the motorcycle messenger who operates from the adjacent offices. Martin's leather jacket, Aztec profile and vigorous bonhomie hold a strange appeal to Gordon, who is happy to drink the hated brew just to be in the same room. And if he manages to drink enough of the stuff one night, he may even pluck up the courage to talk to him. (Martin, it should be said, is only too aware of these attentions, and is thinking of moving to The Marquess of Granby down the road.) In the meantime, should he get a new pair of trainers?

Computers, happily, hold no such complications. In front of his screen, Gordon's power is absolute: every pixel is under his control. Tomorrow morning at nine the intrusions of everyday life will cease to concern him once more as he dives with undisguised relief back into his current project, a space arcade game loosely inspired by lots of other space arcade games. Nothing, not even if it's wearing a leather jacket, will ever make him happier.

M.B.

Mr Stephens

Though Mr Stephens works in a large office – a milieu which might be thought to encourage personal contact – and though he and his wife enjoy the attentions of a wide circle of acquaintances, his most definite characteristic is a tendency to decline invitations. This attitude is all the more remarkable in that it is more or less indiscriminate, applied both to casual solicitations of his company and to more formal events lodged far distant in the calendar. It is all very strange. No matter what the suggestion, however alluring the inducement – it might be a drink after work or a ticket to the firm's dinner dance, three months hence – Mr Stephens is always 'booked up', 'doing something else' or 'otherwise engaged'. Curiously, he can never be persuaded to alter these arrangements.

This blanket prohibition of social activity is bewildering to Mr Stephens' colleagues, many of whom hold him in some regard and would like to further what is no more than a remote acquaintanceship. But though devious traps are set to catch him and elaborate snares contrived to bring him down, it is never any good and Mr Stephens always escapes. More peculiar even than this, perhaps, is the marked air of mystery which hangs over these refusals. For it is a fact that, if pressed by the importunate to attend some social function, he becomes highly evasive, his excuses

lame and his apologies almost perfunctory. As a result his colleagues have formed the impression that he enjoys an extensive social life, but in a sphere he would sooner not disclose. This assumption is broadly correct. Mr Stephens is a Freemason.

In keeping with the rules of his Craft, Mr Stephens does not advertise the fact of this allegiance. He might mention, perhaps, to a friend that he is 'on the square' or 'one of the brotherhood', but more detailed descriptions of his Masonic activities rarely escape him. Mr Stephens is not, to do him justice, one of those Freemasons who gamely supply on tap details of ceremonial handshakes and supposed influence to light-minded questioners. At best he will direct the enquiring to 'one of those books they're always writing about us'. The hint of irony is inescapable. For, like many of his fellow Masons, Mr Stephens is convinced of the existence of a vast anti-Masonic conspiracy, refined by countless television programmes and newspaper exposés and the prurient harrying of public figures whose only failing is that they happen to be 'one of us'. Possibly for this reason he is profoundly hostile to those of his friends who have suggested at one time or another that they might like to become Freemasons themselves. It is, after all, a question of having 'the right motives' as Mr Stephens puts it. There is also the fact that one does not become a Freemason 'just by asking'.

The imputations of exclusivity which these remarks occasionally provoke are hotly resisted by Mr Stephens. He is at pains, for example, to deny the accusation that his innocuous hobby is no more than the ganging up of influential professional men into a closed and slightly sinister organisation administered for their mutual benefit. Mr Stephens points out that the members of his own lodge are united only by their belief in God and by moral probity, that they come from a variety of social and professional backgrounds, and that much of their efforts are devoted to charitable work. He might cautiously acknowledge that Masonic ritual seems 'a bit odd' to outsiders, or recognise that 'this Metropolitan police business', or whatever the current Masonic scandal happens to be, 'hasn't helped', but suggest to him, as mischievous friends occasionally do, that Freemasonry constitutes a secret society and he is liable to turn nasty. Certainly there are rules and regulations: you could find the same thing in a rotary club. Go on to suggest that Freemasonry makes a point of concealing these rules, regulations and practices from all but its initiates and he will get very angry indeed.

Mr Stephens came to Freemasonry in early middle age. As a young man, a promising trainee accountant, he had been a notable sportsman who enjoyed both a game of cricket or a football match and the accompanying camaraderie of the clubhouse. In his thirties, as his ability to compete with energetic younger contemporaries diminished, this interest declined. At the time – he was married by now and the house was on the small side – the suggestion that he should 'go into Masonry' seemed an opportune chance to widen his social circle. Mr Stephens has never regretted this decision, or the tribute – a tribute of time, money and concealment – which it exacted. As he will tell you, with perfect truth, 'some of the best friends I've made have been Freemasons'. Happily he found that Freemasonry, once he had accustomed himself to the bizarre circumstances of his initiation, harboured many of the qualities of the sporting association. Its members convened with agreeable regularity to eat and drink in surroundings of considerable opulence, and caballed enthusiastically in any procedures governing the election of officers and committee members. Mr Stephens entered into these activities with gusto, purchased a pair of white gloves and a Masonic apron from a retiring member of the

Lodge and listened to the accounts of Scribe Ezra and the Architect of the Covenant (for of such did Masonic ritual apparently consist) with avidity. There was a slight problem with his wife, but Mrs Stephens is an indulgent spouse, fond of 'an outing', who relished the chance to dress herself up in any sort of finery; she was soon persuaded to accompany him to the array of social functions at which the presence of women was thought desirable.

Fifteen years have elapsed since Mr Stephens first pulled on his white gloves, adjusted his trouser legs and bared his breast to the initiating officer. Not every aspect of his modest suburban life is entirely to his liking. His children – he is fifty – are in their late teens and chafe to leave home. His 'promise', which turned out not to amount to very much, is unlikely to take him further than the lowly middle manager's job he currently occupies. His colleagues, aware of these constraints, are occasionally perplexed by Mr Stephen's jaunty air, confident demeanour and the impression he conveys of inhabiting a private world filled with rich, inexhaustible incident.

In contrast, Mr Stephen's progress as a member of his Craft has been highly satisfactory. In fact, during a decade and a half as a Freemason he has been Master of his Lodge, accumulated a wide variety of colourful aprons and is spoken of as a racing certainty for Grand Rank. Mr Stephens is justifiably proud of these achievements, which seem to him a wholly adequate recompense for the frustrations of his professional career. He is great at ladies' nights, festive boards and the numerous other diversions with which the Masonic life is attended: an innocent recreation which it would be unworthy to deny.

D.J.T.

Laurence and Suzy

It is Sunday night in a spacious and no more than averagely overpriced pub in Hampstead. Laurence walks in, tossing his car keys from hand to hand. Although he knows many of the people there – large-eyed stubbly young men in tennis shirts, sultry underage girls drenched in expensive scent – he has come specifically to meet Spencer and Nicole, friends and now colleagues at Hill and Borrington, the noted East Finchley ('Highgate borders') estate agents. Laurence has not been with the firm long, but, although a little short of experience in moral blackmail and crass insensitivity, he has already shown such a natural talent for bullying and hectoring that he is very much the coming man.

Laurence progresses to the bar, nods to familiars and banters with friends ('Hi, Terry, how was Florida?'). Ordering an orange juice, he spots Nicole's unconvincingly blonde coiffure and weaves skilfully in its direction. 'Hi!' 'Hi!' 'How are you?' Nicole proffers her cheek, and Laurence kisses the air approximately an inch and a quarter from its surface. Spencer, her boyfriend, holds out his hand; the two colleagues shake vigorously and with feeling. Well over a day has passed since the friends last saw each other.

The conversation is buoyant – Spencer has just sold

a house in Hampstead Garden Suburb, slightly beyond
Hill and Borrington's normal catchment area. And Nicole
also seems livelier than usual: unknown to Laurence, she
has arranged to meet her friend Suzy, whom she knows
Laurence is just going to adore. Indeed, so excited is she
by the prospect that she slurps up her spritzer with rare
gusto, emptying the glass long before Spencer has finished
his Coke.

Finally, Suzy arrives. She too takes five or more minutes
to reach the friends, so many kisses must she blow in the
intervening twenty yards. She has recently given up smok-
ing (she's just dying for a Silk Cut), and must dramatically
reject the dozen or so cigarettes she is offered. Now she
stands, festooned with necklaces and bangles and somehow
balancing a Diet Tango between her talons, while Nicole
introduces this rather good-looking guy with a keen eye
and a simply enormous watch.

As the conversation moves effortlessly round to the
subject of Laurence's new BMW convertible, Spencer and
Nicole silently admire their handiwork. Laurence is tall,
slim, dark and hirsute, with strong features and a small
tuft peeking insouciantly through his shirt. Suzy is slender,
softly pretty and possessed of long and luxuriant curly dark
brown hair, which she tosses meaningfully whenever she
is not sweeping it back from her forehead. Neither her
Louis Vuitton handbag nor the earrings borrowed from
her mother can conceal that she is only seventeen.

Laurence and Suzy meet again the following Thursday,
amongst the milling crowds outside the Dôme. The more
they talk, the more remarkable they find it that they have
never met before. After all, Laurence lives in Edgware, Suzy
in Stanmore, and they know many of the same people. Both
have passed countless Saturday evenings in Stringfellows,
retiring at 4am to the same all-night burger bars along the
Finchley Road. They have even, it turns out, spent many a

Thursday evening amongst the milling crowds outside the Dôme.

But now that they have finally met, they get on well, and find they have much to talk about. Suzy is approaching a significant threshold in her career: when she leaves school the following summer, should she try the fashion business or should she go and work in her father's jewellery firm? Laurence outlines the pros and cons. Both know that her long-term ambitions have little to do with either field of endeavour, and rather more to do with bridal gowns, charge accounts and fitted kitchen suites, but neither finds it necessary to articulate these thoughts.

Over the following weeks Laurence's and Suzy's friends begin to get used to calling them 'Laurence and Suzy'. Without delay, they introduce each other to their parents. Suzy's father admires Laurence's BMW convertible, while Laurence tells Suzy's mother that they look like sisters. The following week Laurence's father offers them tickets to a forthcoming Gloria Estefan gig, while his mother asks Suzy where she got those earrings. All goes smoothly; the parents are impressed. The relationship is sanctioned.

Laurence and Suzy now go out together with increasing frequency – to films, concerts, nightclubs and, for old times' sake, to the Dôme on Thursday. As both live at home, circumstances rarely allow for greater intimacy, although the BMW's tinted windows prove a considerable boon. Laurence buys Suzy gifts; he organises the celebration when she finally passes her driving test. Their mothers occasionally bump into each other in Safeways in Stanmore.

Meanwhile, at school, some of the girls begin to talk of joining a kibbutz after A levels. Suzy is initially horrified – she has, after all, spent many valuable months growing her nails – but the notion of such licensed independence slowly begins to appeal. And she has nothing planned for the summer, although she is thinking about starting her secretarial course (the eventual decision) in the autumn. So why not? But Laurence is less keen. He has just been promoted at Hill and Borrington and he is beginning to feel serious about Suzy. He is almost twenty-four; his parents are keen to put a photocopier in his bedroom and besides, the idea of settling down is not as unattractive as once it might have been.

But Suzy is set on the idea, and the kibbutz is arranged. Six months she will be away, but Laurence promises to wait. He rather suspects it may be a difficult promise to keep, but he promises it anyway.

Suzy leaves, in a suitably emotional farewell. In North London, life goes on. Three weeks later, Suzy is back. Agriculture, she has decided, is not for her. In fact, work generally is not really up her street. And it'll take months to grow her nails back.

But Laurence is not at home. 'I think he's, er, out,' suggests his mother, apparently in a bit of a lather. Suzy remembers: it's Sunday. She'll surprise him. So off she drives (in her mother's Mercedes Sports) to that same spacious and no more than averagely overpriced pub in Hampstead whose customers so blithely ignore the 'Over 21s only' sign on the door. No sign of Spencer, but there's Nicole, and with her, Laurence – except that this time they're not kissing the air. Suzy departs, crushed. She stops on the way home, still crying, for a packet of Marlboro Lights.

A sad story, and one which Suzy's friends will discuss with much amusement in forthcoming weeks. Laurence and Nicole will eventually marry, and Nicole's father, managing director of Hill and Borrington, will eventually bring in Laurence as a full partner. Suzy, meanwhile, reacts in the only way she knows how – by heading straight for South Molton Street with her mother, armed with a fistful of credit cards. With everything that has been going on, she simply can't imagine how she's managed to put up with this old handbag . . .

M.B.

Sue Jenkins

Everybody at St Chad's, from the headmaster and his wife down to the dinner lady and the odd-jobman, admits that Sue has a way with children. The most fractious and sullen small boy becomes charming and voluble when brought into her company. A classroom of unruly nine-year-olds falls silent the moment she appears, displays an almost pathetic eagerness to answer her questions and incubates wild jealousies over the small privileges she allows her more favoured pupils. At any official event or gathering, on Sports Days or annual prizegivings, the children gravitate towards her as if obeying some natural law, cluster around her in their anxiety to impart confidences or merely to share her company. For her own part Sue finds the children 'sweet' and 'wonderful to be with'. She regards the absence of a parent from one of the school's numerous visiting days an act of almost diabolical wickedness.

Such attitudes are not widely in evidence at St Chad's – a middling preparatory school on the Essex/Suffolk border – and for this reason Sue regards certain of her colleagues with scarcely concealed distaste. Her fellow teachers tend to be men, of either extreme youth or advanced age. Neither category, Sue imagines, 'really knows how to treat the children' or 'really cares about them'. Several admit that they are doing the job simply because no

other form of employment was available. All not only do merely what is required of them but would rather be doing something else. Sue finds this indifference mildly shocking. In contrast, her own attitude to her work is characterised by a cheerful disregard for hours and contractual stipulations, and she will happily give up long stretches of her spare time, often without charge, to coach examination candidates or accompany school teams to away matches.

This commitment to the interests of her charges has deep roots. Like many people involved in education she has her own theories about children: much of Sue's leisure time, in fact, is taken up in reading illustrated treatises on child care or rather forbidding books of infant psychology. Typically these stress the importance of furnishing a 'proper childhood' and 'giving the child friends' and in this recreation, perhaps, lies the origin of her own uncommon abilities. Sue was an only child herself, the product of a late marriage by two parents who were almost middle-aged by the time of her birth. Though there was indulgence – and Sue remains on the friendliest terms with her mother and father – it did not extend to any attempt to supply her with the company of other children. Her parents were formal and rather reserved people who 'kept themselves to themselves'. They had few relatives and such social activities as they allowed each other seldom admitted the presence of a small child. In consequence, Sue passed a lonely and rather circumscribed childhood, in which there was affection and kindness, but very little resembling wider human contact.

This early isolation was reinforced by family circumstance. Sue's father worked as the Home Counties representative of a light-engineering firm, a good job for the time – this was the early sixties and the engineering boom was in full swing – but one which demanded frequent removals around the outer London suburbs. From Harrow to

Hounslow, from Ruislip to Sydenham, the transfers came annually, their prospect lending an air of transience to the most solid family dwelling. Subsequently when she came to collate her early memories, Sue became aware that most of them had to do with moving house. Such migrations were usually sufficient to sever the casual associations of childhood. The new school, the likely looking girl next door, the distant cousin found living three streets away: it was rare for opportunities of this sort to survive the restrictions of enforced departure. Moreover, such entertainments as Sue cared to offer her few acquaintances were invariably beset by difficulties. Mrs Jenkins, a punctilious housewife, 'couldn't abide', as she put it, the thought of children 'messing up her nice clean house'. As a result, the few parties and social gatherings of Sue's early adolescence took place in, and were generally extinguished by, an atmosphere of nervous tension. Eventually they ceased altogether.

Curiously, set down in this unpromising environment, transported from house to house and school to school – where her attempts to impinge on the long-established friendships of other children rarely succeeded – Sue did not repine. She was a good-humoured girl, regretted her mum's 'nerves', sympathised with her dad and his endless trawl around the manufacturing workshops of south-east England. To compensate herself for this neglect she resorted to the traditional expedients of the lonely child, cultivating intense relationships with her toys and with a succession of imaginary familiars. Agreeably, she found that these substitutes went some way towards solacing her desire for companionship and that in devising medicinal rituals for a sick doll or imparting the rudiments of arithmetic to a sofa full of stuffed animals she became gratifyingly absorbed. Several of her teaching formulae – and almost every variant of her classroom style – are derived from these early experiments.

There was never the slightest chance, as Sue grew older, of her seeking any career which did not involve the care and instruction of children. In adolescence – Dad had retired by then and they were living a more settled life in Essex – while her contemporaries attended discotheques and coffee bars, she went out babysitting and helped with the local cub pack. Similarly, while her schoolfriends took Saturday jobs as waitresses and shop assistants or worked in the holidays as temporary librarians, her own part-time employment was of the most regimented cast: child-minding, playground supervision, a blissful summer, once, as the assistant warden of an adventure playground. Later, when the question of further education arose – she was a bright girl who could have gone to university – Sue applied instead for a place at the teacher training college nearest to her home. (The event prompted a rare disagreement with Mum and Dad who, backed up by puzzled school teachers, couldn't understand why 'someone of your ability' should so wilfully decline to 'do better for herself'.) At college Sue flourished as in no previous medium, won the golden opinions of her tutors and gained a highly creditable degree. From the various schools which offered her employment she selected St Chad's on the grounds of its convenient location – near, but not too near, Mr and Mrs Jenkins and the retirement bungalow at Chelmsford.

The best part of a decade later, her original pupils grown into hulking teenagers (they write to her occasionally, a gesture she finds 'sweet') Sue sees no reason to alter what is altogether an agreeable way of life. Her employer is very pleased with her – for good reason, as a high proportion of her extra-curricular duties are performed *gratis* – and, fearful that she might be enticed away to some rival establishment, frequently rewards her with small tokens of prestige and common-room status. She is, it goes without saying, badly paid. However, the school allows her free accommodation and by denying herself 'luxuries', defined as new clothes and foreign holidays, she can narrowly afford to run a small car. Maintaining this vehicle and paying for its many minor repairs occupies much of her spare time and takes up much of her expenditure, but there is the fact that without it she would not be able to transport her cricket teams or make the frequent journeys to visit her parents (Mum and Dad are getting on now and would be mortally offended if she didn't come home at the weekends). Consequently, Sue accepts the stringent personal economies which its ownership demands without complaint.

In her late twenties, blonde, plump and unfailingly even-tempered, she is not without admirers. In fact, there are plenty of young men temporarily becalmed on the school's staff who would be glad to take her into Colchester of an evening or buy her drinks and meals in the restaurants of the vicinity. But somehow these encounters never come to much. For one thing Sue is pretty absorbed in her work and the young man who arrives at seven imagining that he can enjoy her company for the evening is quite likely to find himself sandwiched between an hour's marking and the parent–teacher association ceilidh. Then there is the undoubted fact that she is rather a bore on the subject of small boys. Sue does not regret these fragmentary relationships with the opposite sex. The suspicion that she might have fallen prematurely into an inescapable rut has yet to alarm her and she is enjoying what in all likelihood will prove to be the happiest period of her life. For, despite the possibility that she will never have any of her own, Sue has a way with children.

D.J.T.

Geoff

No one, Geoff used to say, becomes fat overnight. It is a gradual process, a slow but inexorable spread of excess adipose tissue across all the body's most vulnerable outposts. First comes the paunch, enveloping the unsuspecting abdomen and stealthily asserting its right to burst zips in public and make travelling in lifts an uncomfortably tactile experience. Next to manifest themselves are the more subtle symptoms of weight gain: thigh expansion, upper-arm wobble ('look, it's all muscle') and, finally and most visibly, radically improved suspension in the buttock department.

But it's not until after a particularly large lunch, when you have emptied the plate and indeed the room of everything remotely edible, that the vital decision begins to loom. Are you just someone who happens to be fat, your weight being a function of the amount you eat and no more? Or are you, by contrast, a fat person, someone whose very being is governed by fatness? In short, is it your weight problem, or everybody else's? It's a knotty dilemma, and only when you have properly sorted it out in your mind can you get on with the serious business of ordering pudding.

Geoff, for instance, is not someone who just happens to be fat. He is proud to be fat. Some men, he would say, are born fat. Some achieve fatness. And some have

fatness thrust upon them. Looking at Geoff these days, most impartial observers tend to assume that he falls into all three categories.

Geoff is not, however, absurdly fat: he can still walk reasonable distances unaided and was briefly seen to run a year ago last March, when a neighbour's Dobermann turned inconveniently nasty. But years of dedicated eating, combined with a recently acquired (but nonetheless vigorous) contempt for exercise, have added an impressive bulk to his person. Oceans of cellulite flow unhindered across his frame, some settling in relatively unusual places. Although many of his friends are equally well upholstered, Geoff is, for instance, the only person he knows with fat knees.

Not that he was ever this way. In his youth – he is only thirty-two, but his best years are generally agreed to be behind him – he was stocky but lean, thanks to a year-long teenage flirtation with bodybuilding, followed by a strict regimen of winter rugby and summer cricket. Such an efficient machine needs regular refuelling, and early in his athletic career he developed a robust enthusiasm for post-match curries and their traditional accompaniment, uncountable gallons of lager.

But when he married, Geoff suddenly discovered that at weekends there was rather more to do than play sport. On Saturdays he was expected to help with the shopping, while on Sundays there was always something that needed doing around the house – if, that is, the wife's parents weren't coming round for lunch. Leisure time, it appeared, was far too valuable to be wasted on leisure, and Geoff's sporting life was his first and greatest sacrifice. His appearances for the local teams became increasingly infrequent, and with momentum lost, Geoff also waved farewell to form, fitness and finally even enthusiasm. Within three years of marriage he had given up sport altogether. Not wishing to lose touch with his sporting roots entirely, though, he retained his keenness for curries and lager, adding the menu of the nearby Berni Inn to his expanding repertoire. His wife, whose unusual thinness had caused her to be overfed since birth (to no visible effect), happily supplied the magnitude of portion that would satisfy her rapidly swelling husband.

Today Geoff stands in the playground of the local park, pondering on the ultimate awfulness of life and listening to his own stomach rumbling. His children, plump mannikins both, chase each other around his impressively broad legs, whooping and screeching with pleasure, but Geoff is cross. Many things irritate him – it's too hot, there are too many people around, it's hours until dinner – but what really gets up his nose are other people's preconceptions of him as a fat person. Just a moment ago old Mrs Barnacle from the Post Office passed by and gave him a cheery, friendly grin, assuming that Geoff, being a fat person, would naturally be a cheery, friendly person. But Geoff is not. He is irritable, impatient and extremely peckish. Constantly expected to be easy-going, lovable and an unceasing source of fun and merriment, he responds by being rude, overbearing and occasionally violent. Unknown children who catch his eye flee to his parents' arms, blubbing.

Is it all a front? Is Geoff really a sensitive, spiritual sort of fellow, beloved by elderly relatives and forever kind to small furry animals (alive and uncooked)? Sadly not. For him, asserting his fatness is a lifetime's task, never completed. His voice is loud and aggressive, his body language threatening. On public transport, he sprawls like a truculent porpoise, ensuring that no one else can sit on those benches marked '4 SEATS'. In pubs, he perches precariously on a stool, spreading himself across the bar whenever anyone tries to order a drink. In cinemas, he blocks everybody's view, eats popcorn at full volume and snores during action sequences. On holiday, he leaps paunch first into swimming pools, soaking all within a thirty-yard radius.

Throughout all life's minor battles, Geoff wields his paunch like an offensive weapon. It has long replaced his penis (now lost within the folds below) as the epicentre of his manhood. If it hit you, you'd certainly know about it. Whether Geoff would, though, is a different matter entirely.

His health, not unreasonably, is a cause of concern to him, although after a dozen pints of Spankworth's most such worries conveniently recede. Sex, once the source of many minutes' harmless ecstasy, now presents awkward topological problems (he can get it up, but can he get it in?). Work occupies him in a desultory way, but only until lunch. His wife, increasingly cowed, tolerates all this with equanimity. His children are too busy eating to notice anything else.

But Geoff is a man with a mission. Being fat may have changed his life, and possibly reduced it by a third or so, but it has done wonders for his fundamental misanthropy. Indeed, he is determined that the stereotype of the obese chucklesome oaf should be destroyed forever. As he contemplates these pleasing thoughts, an ice-cream van drives shrilly into the park. Visions of a triple 99 (with chocolate sauce) float temptingly into his mind, and the blanket of contingency, as he jangles in his pocket for change, descends upon him once again.

M.B.

Mr Grainger

Take a train from Liverpool Street to Norwich, change at Norwich station and take another train westward through the level Norfolk countryside towards the market towns of Wymondham and Downham and there is a fair chance that the land through which you travel – acres of even farmland dotted with windmills and distant church spires – will belong to Mr Grainger. It is a tight, well-ordered vista, this, where neatly planted fields of barley alternate with the lush squares of pasturage, where the hint of ulterior design in the layout of the landscape is strong, and even the files of scrubby trees – larch, spruce and the odd surviving elm – have a suspicious regularity: a tamed and somehow regimented slice of rural England. Uniform, monotonous, the whole suggesting a ground plan by the Queen of Brobdingnag, Mr Grainger's fields nevertheless possess a distinct, if seasonal, charm. In early summer, when the barley flares up six feet high and the cows huddle beneath the shadow of the railway bank, the effect on the coast-bound traveller is seldom less than gratifying.

Mr Grainger views the situation somewhat differently. There are the cows, for instance: 'Nobody ever made any money out of dairy farming,' he will inform the casual listener. 'Two hundred head of stock out there eating their heads off and I'm losing money on every one of them.' Then there is the barley. 'A good harvest? I daresay there may be a good harvest. Try telling that to folk who have to sell it. People can't expect to go on eating bread unless they're prepared to pay a proper price for it.' Even the soft fruit – formerly an intensely lucrative standby – isn't what it was now that Channings have shut their jam factory in King's Lynn. As Mr Grainger is known to be the wealthiest landowner for twenty miles, these remarks are not treated with complete seriousness. However, the relentless litany of complaint is an important part of his allure as a host. Buttressed by these recitations he cuts an impressive, if lugubrious, figure at the dinner tables of northwest Norfolk: a man bloodied by the batterings of savage natural forces and unrelenting economic caprice, but apparently unbowed.

Given the astonishing series of vicissitudes with which he is annually visited, given floods, droughts and mad cow disease, given above all the sparseness of financial rewards, it might be wondered why Mr Grainger persists so steadfastly in the cultivation of his demesne. If he is to be believed, the answer lies almost solely in his elevated conception of duty. Mr Grainger talks a great deal about 'duty'. There is, for instance, the duty of the farmer, both to the nation ('How else are people to feed themselves I'd like to know?') and the land ('People talk a lot about *preserving the countryside*. Who else preserves it apart from us farmer folk I'd like to know?'). But there is also the duty of the farmer to the Government ('We don't want hand-outs, we want a proper investment in the agricultural community'). Above all, perhaps, there is the duty of Government and nation to the farmer. Mr Grainger feels strongly that the public ('ordinary folk') ought to realise that there is a tribute to be paid for the food they consume and vouchsafe a little more gratitude to those who supply it (in practice, this would mean submitting uncomplainingly to higher food prices but Mr Grainger is too wise a man to say so). At other times he will talk feelingly of the 'shameful contract' – Mr Grainger has his elevated moments – which currently operates between the nation and its farmers. Mr Grainger is an accomplished if rough-hewn speaker and seldom fails to move an audience. The wonder, according to the guests who assemble in his roomy farmhouse – or at any rate to those with no knowledge of farming – is that he has survived so long in the face of such unpromising circumstances.

And yet Mr Grainger has survived, if not triumphantly then indefatigably. He is not quite a veteran – there are seventy- and eighty-year-olds in this part of Norfolk still bringing in the beet harvest – but it is many years since young Tom Grainger, as he then was, came back from National Service and succeeded his dad in the management of the Hall Farm, as it then was. On his return to Norfolk and his inheritance, Mr Grainger found that his prospects were far from promising. In fact they were not promising at all. Old Mr Grainger, baffled by the war and the succeeding years of austerity, had let things slide. Worse, his son discovered, the land was not even his own, possession still residing in the hands of a faded 'county' family two miles distant and requiring the payment of a nominal rent. It is not going too far to say that Mr Grainger's patrimony, circa 1954, consisted of little more than half a dozen fields of arable, a herd of spindly dairy cows and some agricultural implements dating back to the time of the First World War. A lesser man might have sold the goodwill and departed, yet Mr Grainger hung on. As a schoolboy and again as an agricultural student, his limited intellectual abilities had been compensated for by profound powers of application. Now, in adversity, he did not repine: he merely persevered. Since that time his career has followed a remorseless trajectory. Thirty-five years on he farms

2,000 acres – a vast principality of arable and pasture, a township of barns and outhouses – and, could, he is fond of saying, spend a day walking round his own perimeters if he wished. Mr Grainger is fat now and sedentary, and this is not an excursion that he has undertaken for some considerable time.

It has been a laborious progress, requiring the continual deployment of Mr Grainger's deep reserves of native cunning. He began in a small way, by acquiring a brace of adjoining properties from a bankrupt smallholder. Devious litigation with the county family, its male stock depleted and impoverished by the war, secured him the freehold and further acreage extending almost to the manorial front door (the Hall stands empty now and tenantless: Mr Grainger would have knocked it down long ago were it not for a timely preservation order). Having acquired the land it was next necessary to obtain the means of cultivating it. The Hall Farm's staff at this juncture consisted of two elderly labourers. Mr Grainger looked about him with a circumspect eye. He needed labour – the expensive machinery which would replace labour was as yet a remote ambition – and he needed it cheaply, better still unorganised. The influence of the Agricultural Workers' Union was at this time, in this part of Norfolk, very strong. Greatly daring, Mr Grainger let it be known that he would decline to recognise it. The ensuing struggle was protracted. There were strikes and lock-outs. Hard words were exchanged in village streets. There was even, one dark November night, the firing of a barn, but Mr Grainger stood his ground, though for a time he thought it unwise to set forth outside his gates without a shotgun. He has had no trouble 'from that quarter', as he puts it, for thirty years.

The decisions which Mr Grainger had to make at this period of his life – harsh decisions involving tied cottages and morose tenants – were not arrived at without a struggle. Neither were they undertaken without frequent invocations of Mr Grainger's 'duty'. He was aware of the nature of his responsibilities to those he employed. His innate conservatism made him reluctant to tamper with the old order of things. But then duty – and responsibility – worked both ways. Mr Grainger did not state in so many words that he who paid the piper called the tune, but the concept was never far distant from his dealings with his tenantry. There was, too, at this time another sort of duty with which he found himself invested: the need to achieve maximum yields from the very limited resources at his disposal. He accepted, not without a certain degree of misgiving, the advice given to him by Government scientists of the day and he made one or two little experiments in this line without recourse to officialdom. He bought pesticides and exfoliants. He ceased to follow his father's practice of crop rotation and invested heavily in fertilisers and nutrient enhancers. The Norfolk County Council, of which Mr Grainger became a member at about this time, grew used to his homilies on the subject of 'modern farming' and 'commercial exploitation of land'.

For Mr Grainger the 1950s were a period of consolidation. In the 1960s and 70s, however, he flourished as never before. He discovered, to his agreeable surprise, that the Government was prepared to pay him whatever emoluments he required to produce vital foodstuffs and to subsidise their production handsomely. (Mr Grainger became something of an expert on government grants and was supposed to have refurbished his combine harvester fleet entirely at the public expense.) Subsequently he discovered the existence of European Commissioners who were content, inexplicably, to pay him equally large sums not to produce these items. The profits from this largesse allowed him to mechanise, and to sack most of his manual staff. Yet his misgivings remained. This was the 1960s and the phrase 'environmental concern' scarcely existed, but Mr Grainger was a countryman at heart and it pained him, or he thought it pained him, to deposit exfoliants in the streams which passed through his land, pained him to chop down trees, to plough kale that could have been eaten by human beings back into the ground as fertiliser. Mr Grainger justified these activities to himself on the grounds of expedience, the balancing of a lesser evil with a greater good. 'How are you to make an omelette without breaking eggs, I'd like to know?' he was fond of enquiring when the talk turned to environmental pollution. To one who made his livelihood from the soil, much-canvassed 'alternative' methods of agricultural production seemed faintly ridiculous. It is amusing, even now, to hear the rancour which Mr Grainger can bring to a topic such as 'organic farming'. ('Using old breadcrusts for fertiliser. How's that going to produce a field of spring barley I'd like to know?')

As it is, Mr Grainger would like to know rather a lot of things: questions which in these latter days are specific and urgent rather than merely rhetorical. What have the unacceptably high levels of nitrate in the local water supply got to do with him, he would like to know? Why should the Campaign for the Preservation of Rural England think him a fitting target for their impertinent letters? Why are the soil biologists from the local research station (who twenty years ago were happy to supply him with any nutrient he demanded) so eager to shake their heads over the samples from the Lower Field? In happier times he might have found an answer from the County Council – Mr Grainger retains his seat, precariously – but, alas, in these uncertain days, a greenish tinge hangs over that bastion of rural inertia. On the day on which the Anglian Water Authority's demand for an investigation into river pollution was officially ratified Mr Grainger gave local government up for lost.

In cash terms Mr Grainger is worth perhaps a million pounds. His land is worth at least twice this. Despite this affluence his private life is painfully unostentatious. Mr Grainger buys a new car once every five years, rarely takes holidays and has worn the same green corduroy suit for as long as anyone can remember. Though he is a convivial host, fond of entertaining neighbouring farmers and their wives, it is noticeable that the farmhouse carpets are practically threadbare and that there is a makeshift air to some of the furniture. Mrs Grainger, an early acquisition, is a homely woman, whose conversation seldom leaves the topic of her grandchildren. Mr Grainger is at his best on these occasions, his grievances temporarily forgotten, secure in the company of ancient cronies whose farming lives in many cases predate his own, but he is rarely content. Perhaps it is the fault of this galloping greenery. He cannot be sure. At any rate, looking back over a robust and prosperous career, pondering a lifetime of bruising responsibilities, Mr Grainger is perhaps a little too conscious that his chief duty has been neither to government nor nation, but to himself.

D.J.T.

Charlie

Charlie opened his eyes. The exhausted but ecstatic woman clutching him to her warm and shapely breast – even in pregnancy she had retained admirable control over her body weight – was, he presumed, his mother. And the dork behind the video camera, the one shouting 'Hold him up a bit . . . yeh yeh . . . that's fine . . . cheer up for Christ's sake' – he had to be the father.

On balance Charlie preferred his mother, flushed and strained though she undoubtedly was. A precocious child, he swiftly recognised that he was not seeing her at her best. But at least he could now see her. During the birth the room had been almost completely dark, with classical music blaring from invisible speakers, the endless intolerable labour interrupted only by his mother's anguished cries ('I want an epidural!') and his father's calm explanations ('It isn't in the birth plan, darling'). Amidst all the mess and the blood and the placenta and the violins, the whirring of the video camera had been almost soothing.

But now Charlie lay safe in his mother's arms, watching his father's frantic activity and the crisp efficiency of the nurses, who strode to and fro carrying equipment while the doctors languished, awaiting compliments. His mother and father had gone private for the birth – 'money well spent' as they had told their friends – although during

the birth itself Charlie's father had seemed rather more interested in the bill than in Charlie. But now, expense forgotten, that long-suppressed desire to be Francis Ford Coppola had come to the fore. It seemed like hours before he finally got bored and announced that he had to go to work because he had an important meeting.

The next few days were uncommonly pleasant – Charlie's birth had been mercifully without complications – and soon it was time to go 'home', an overmortgaged maisonette in Islington. Charlie was deposited in a Moses basket (complete with leather handles) and placed in the back of the company car, where he soon dozed off. He awoke in a cot in a newly decorated nursery. Babar the elephant was the room's theme.

As the weeks drifted by, Charlie enjoyed his mother's attentions, particularly the breast-feeding, about which she initially seemed very enthusiastic. But as the time-consuming nature of the task (not to mention its destructive effect on her social life) began to stifle this eagerness, Charlie found himself entrusted to the care of a maternity nurse, hired to clamp the bottle to his mouth every three hours or so whether he was hungry or not. Charlie enjoyed crying – it was less boring than just lying there smiling inanely – but this ruthless regimen exhausted even his capacity for noise pollution. To make matters worse, the ugliness of his nurse was in stark contrast to the ethereal beauty of his mother, who had conducted the interviews for the post.

But his mother was far too busy now, what with her mother-and-baby social events, postnatal exercises and all that shopping to do. One day a proper large pram with huge swirly wheels was delivered, but swiftly taken away again when it failed to fit through the front door. And Charlie's clothes were as chic as could be – Giorgio Armani's new baby couture was much favoured, as was anything featuring Babar the elephant.

At social events he lay gurgling, evilly refuting his mother's vindictive claims that he cried from morning till night, and then from night till morning as well just to make sure everyone had got the message. Meanwhile all the mothers discussed the controversial issues of the moment: anaesthetics, their scars and the impossibility of finding a good nanny nowadays.

Charlie was, of course, a green baby (better than a blue baby, his father joked, to angry silence). None of his baby-food jars contained artificial preservatives (or glass, as his father quipped after a particularly hard day at work), and his 'Econappies' were kind to the environment in a way that his mother, when pressed, could never quite recall.

After the maternity nurse, a nanny arrived, an eighteen-year-old Norwegian who spent many hours of the day, when the rest of the flat was empty, telephoning her boyfriend in Trondheim. She at least was easier to charm than the maternity nurse – it seemed that she actually liked babies, even if she was not too sure which way up to hold them – but with his mother out of the flat for long periods, Charlie began to notice that crying was not proving as effective as it had been. Another, more subtle tactic was called for.

Fortunately, it was at this stage in his development that Charlie became aware of an even more powerful weapon at his disposal: vomit. Almost at will, he found, he could direct a small blob of undigested Cow & Gate at virtually any target within six feet, with sometimes spectacular results. Particularly successful targets included: his father's new tie; his mother's cleavage; his grand-mother's cup of tea; his smelly great-uncle's hair; the tub of houmous (who could tell the difference?); the sofa; the wall; and, his perennial favourite, the carpet. After disgorging such an emission, Charlie would smile inno-cently, implying with his expression that someone else had done it. Somehow he managed to elude serious punishment.

Soon his father was coming home at all hours of the day because his mother 'couldn't cope with it all', although it remained unclear precisely what 'it all' consisted of. She wanted to go back to work, it seemed, to escape the horrors of home. She needed her career: she did not want to turn into a vegetable. Charlie was now walking quite efficiently, and breaking an average of two valuable ornaments a day. It was time for him to be sent to Tumbletots.

And now, a year or so later, Charlie is joyously ensconced at nursery school, eating crayons, kicking smaller children and forgetting his toilet training whenever it suits him. The nanny has been sent back to Trondheim, and a more malleable au pair is in situ. But all is not peaceful in that overmortgaged maisonette in Islington. His mother, back at work a mere four months, is not feeling well. His father, who is still paying off the hospital bill, is not feeling well either. Now it's not only Charlie who is throwing up all over the place. Yes, the whole process is starting all over again.

This time, she says, she's definitely having an epidural.

M.B.

A NOTE ON THE AUTHORS

D. J. Taylor was born in Norwich in 1960 and educated at Norwich School and St John's College, Oxford, where he read modern history. He is the author of a novel, *Great Eastern Land* (1986), and a critical study, *A Vain Conceit: British Fiction in the 1980s* (1989). He is married and lives in London.

Marcus Berkmann was born in London in 1960, and was educated at Highgate School and Worcester College, Oxford, where he read mathematics. He is a regular contributor to the *Spectator*, the *Daily Mail* and *Punch*, and has written two series of the Radio 4 comedy series *Lenin of the Rovers*. He is unmarried, and owns only one suit.